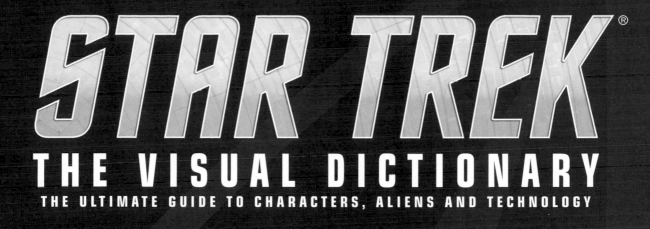

STAR TREK®

THE VISUAL DICTIONARY

THE ULTIMATE GUIDE TO CHARACTERS, ALIENS AND TECHNOLOGY

Sagittal ridge

Klingons lack tear ducts

Klingon heart has eight chambers

Dk'tahg blade

Baldric bears symbols of noble house and rank

24th century Klingon Defence Force uniform

Retractable side blades

Spiked fingerless gauntlets for hand-to-hand combat

KLINGON

Fires a beam that tears the target apart

VARON-T DISRUPTOR

Injects delta isotopes into the subject to cause time shifts

TIME-TRAVEL ARMBAND

Serrations intended to cause maximum injury

Klingon script

KLINGON BLADE

Inflicts pain without causing lasting damage

CARDASSIAN TORTURE IMPLEMENTS

Typically rugged Klingon technology

KLINGON TRICORDER

When mixed together, perfumes become lethal

FLAXIAN ASSASSIN'S PERFUME CASE

Gambling is a major part of Ferengi culture

FERENGI GAME

STAR TREK®

THE VISUAL DICTIONARY

THE ULTIMATE GUIDE TO CHARACTERS, ALIENS AND TECHNOLOGY

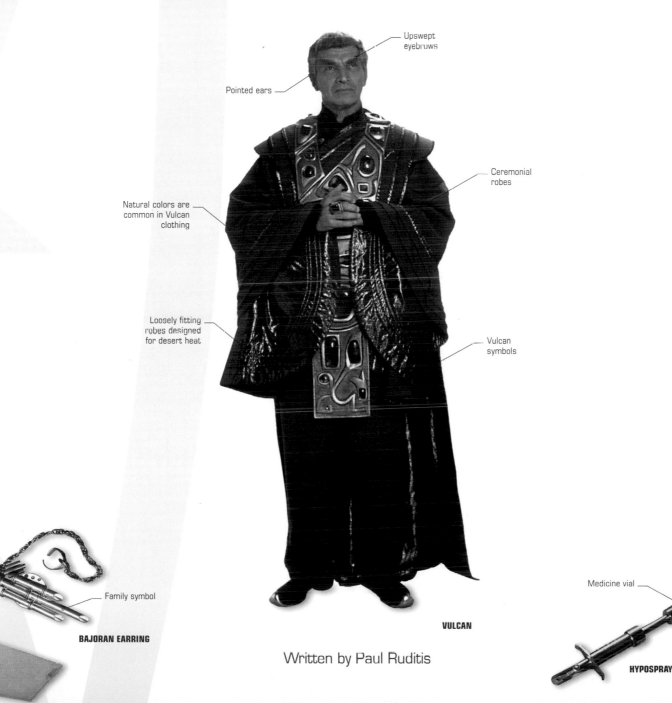

Upswept
eyebrows

Pointed ears

Ceremonial
robes

Natural colors are
common in Vulcan
clothing

Loosely fitting
robes designed
for desert heat

Vulcan
symbols

Family symbol

BAJORAN EARRING

VULCAN

Medicine vial

HYPOSPRAY

Written by Paul Ruditis

CONTENTS

FOREWORD BY JOHN DE LANCIE

Greetings from Beyond.

"You have no idea what you've gotten yourself into," were the words that came wafting into my ear on that early June morning in 1987. I was standing on the sound stage at Paramount Studios, three days into shooting *Encounter at Farpoint*. When I turned around, a tall gentleman with an all-knowing grin stood before me. "What do you mean?" I asked. "Oh, you'll find out" he said chuckling and walked away. "You'll find out."

It's been twenty-five years since Gene Roddenberry made that prophetic statement. At the time, I had no idea what he meant, but today I think I do. He wasn't talking about *Star Trek* the juggernaut; he was talking about the people who love *Star Trek*. He was talking about the fans. Over the years, I've had the opportunity to meet those fans – thousands of them – at airports, restaurants, hospitals, classrooms, gas stations, grocery stores, on the bridge of a destroyer, even in the throne room of a king and, to this day, I am amazed at how *Star Trek* has enriched their lives in so many different way and, in turn, my own.

Of course, it's no wonder so many of these lovers of *Star Trek* turned their passion for the show into a passion for science. You don't have to go much further than NASA, JPL or Caltech to find a lot of *Star Trek* fans. Nor is it surprising that a generation of budding technologists who embraced the show in the 60s, with its array of wondrous gadgets, had an active role in bringing those gadgets to reality in the 90s. They are the expected lovers of *Star Trek* – the sci-fi enthusiasts who, like myself, loved all things futuristic. But, truth be told, I still don't think that's whom Gene had in mind when he teased me with, "you'll find out." I think he was alluding to people like the woman I met who was confined to a wheelchair with MS and who, with gnarled hands, handed me a note that read: "For one hour a week, *Star Trek* allows me to soar to the heavens and forget the body that imprisons me." Or the old barber in Damascus, Syria who proudly told me he had learned to speak English by watching every episode of *Star Trek* he could find. Or the parent of the mentally challenged teenager who brought her son to a *Star Trek* convention and, with tears in her eyes, watched as the other *Star Trek* fans so willingly included him. This is what Gene was talking about.

Star Trek may profess to explore alien planets but it is our own inner-selves that it really explores. Gene created a show and the fans created the community. That is what makes *Star Trek* so unique. He built it and they came from every walk of life.

Star Trek is more than the sum of its parts. *Star Trek* is a ticket into the world of imagination. It is an invitation to dream, and wonder and ask, "What if?" It is a super nova that brightly shines in our night sky affirming the hope that our future – through science and technology, through tolerance and acceptance, through courage and perseverance – will be better for everyone.

I like to think that I'm part of that future and I know that you, who are reading this wonderful book, are part of it too.

Live Long and Dream.

John de Lancie

THE FINAL FRONTIER

HUMANS FIRST VENTURED into space in the mid-20th century. They sent up satellites, orbited the Earth in rockets, and landed ships on the Moon. A hundred years later they created the first vessel capable of flying faster than the speed of light. And they soon learned that they were not alone. An immeasurable number of alien races populated the Galaxy. Some would become friends, while others would be enemies. The Human desire for exploration continued to grow as they brought together their galactic neighbours and developed technology that would take them even beyond the stars.

THE MILKY WAY GALAXY

The Milky Way is the Human name for the Galaxy in which most known life-forms exist. It is divided into four quadrants: The Alpha Quadrant, which is the seat of the Federation; The Beta Quadrant, which houses additional Federation members and non-member races like the Klingons and Romulans; and the Gamma and Delta Quadrants, which are so distant that extraordinary measures, such as the Bajoran Wormhole, are required to visit them.

THE FEDERATION

UNITED FEDERATION of PLANETS

FLAG OF THE FEDERATION

In the year 2155 a Coalition of Planets was formed between the Humans and their closest alien allies, the Vulcans, Andorians and Tellarites. That Coalition was soon tested when another alien race, the Romulans, declared war on Earth. Even while under attack, Humans prevailed in keeping the Coalition governments united and succeeded in defeating the Romulans. As a result of this war, the Coalition members amended their original charter to agree to protect each other in times of conflict, as they worked jointly to explore the galaxy. All member worlds would have equal rank in this new organization that would become known as the United Federation of Planets. It has grown considerably in the centuries since, and now spans over 8,000 light years.

DOMINION SPACE

END OF BAJORAN WORMHOLE DISTANCE: 70,000 LIGHT YEARS

GAMMA QUADRANT

GALACTIC CORE

ALPHA QUADRANT

BAJORAN WORMHOLE

CARDASSIAN UNION

SOL SYSTEM (FEDERATION/STARFLEET HQ)

EARTH
To acknowledge the vital role Humans played in the formation of the Federation, Earth was chosen as its capital planet. By the 23rd century Earth is effectively a paradise, free of all poverty or war. The office of the Federation President is located in Paris, France while Starfleet Headquarters is in San Francisco, U.S.A.

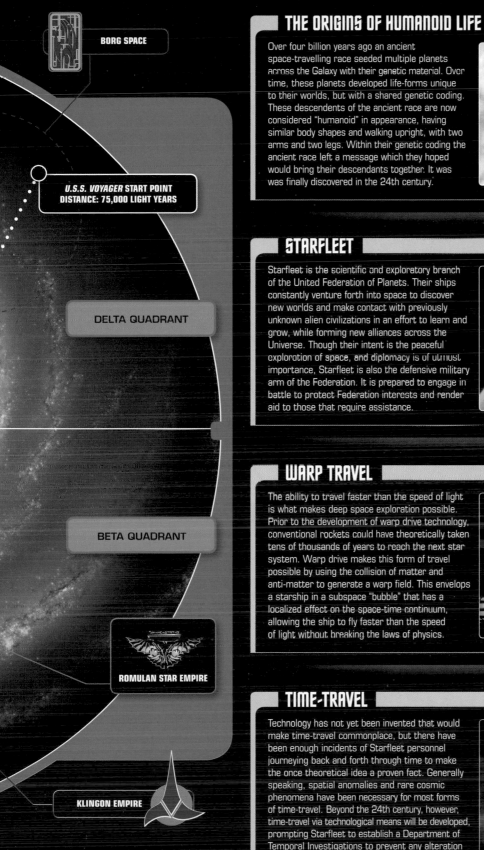

**U.S.S. VOYAGER START POINT
DISTANCE: 75,000 LIGHT YEARS**

DELTA QUADRANT

BETA QUADRANT

ROMULAN STAR EMPIRE

KLINGON EMPIRE

* Positions approximate

THE ORIGINS OF HUMANOID LIFE

Over four billion years ago an ancient space-travelling race seeded multiple planets across the Galaxy with their genetic material. Over time, these planets developed life-forms unique to their worlds, but with a shared genetic coding. These descendents of the ancient race are now considered "humanoid" in appearance, having similar body shapes and walking upright, with two arms and two legs. Within their genetic coding the ancient race left a message which they hoped would bring their descendants together. It was was finally discovered in the 24th century.

STARFLEET

Starfleet is the scientific and exploratory branch of the United Federation of Planets. Their ships constantly venture forth into space to discover new worlds and make contact with previously unknown alien civilizations in an effort to learn and grow, while forming new alliances across the Universe. Though their intent is the peaceful exploration of space, and diplomacy is of utmost importance, Starfleet is also the defensive military arm of the Federation. It is prepared to engage in battle to protect Federation interests and render aid to those that require assistance.

WARP TRAVEL

The ability to travel faster than the speed of light is what makes deep space exploration possible. Prior to the development of warp drive technology, conventional rockets could have theoretically taken tens of thousands of years to reach the next star system. Warp drive makes this form of travel possible by using the collision of matter and anti-matter to generate a warp field. This envelops a starship in a subspace "bubble" that has a localized effect on the space-time continuum, allowing the ship to fly faster than the speed of light without breaking the laws of physics.

TIME-TRAVEL

Technology has not yet been invented that would make time-travel commonplace, but there have been enough incidents of Starfleet personnel journeying back and forth through time to make the once theoretical idea a proven fact. Generally speaking, spatial anomalies and rare cosmic phenomena have been necessary for most forms of time-travel. Beyond the 24th century, however, time-travel via technological means will be developed, prompting Starfleet to establish a Department of Temporal Investigations to prevent any alteration of the established timeline.

HUMANS

HUMANS (ALSO KNOWN AS TERRANS) have always been the heart of the Federation. Overcoming a history of violent conflict, they were largely responsible for bringing together the alien races that formed the first Coalition of Planets. This eventually grew to include over 150 worlds functioning under a unified central government. Their homeworld, Earth, is located in the Sol System, which is designated as Sector 001 to reflect that it is the seat of the Federation President and legislature.

STARFLEET HEADQUARTERS
Starfleet, the scientific and exploratory arm of the Federation, is based on Earth. It is on an unending mission to explore strange new worlds, seek out new life and new civilizations, and boldly go where no one has gone before.

HUMAN PHYSIOLOGY

Humans, like many other species, descend from an ancient race of interstellar travellers that seeded their DNA on planets across the Galaxy. Common traits among these races are that they are humanoid, bipedal, often mammalian, and tend to live on worlds with oxygen-nitrogen rich atmospheres (designated as Class-M planets). Humans tend to have average physical abilities when compared to other alien races. For instance, they are not as strong as Klingons, but they are better able to adapt to cold temperatures. Thanks to medical advancements, by the 24th century a Human lifespan can reach over 140 years.

Beagle

DOMESTICATED ANIMALS
For thousands of years, and into the 24th century, Humans have domesticated animals to use for food, to ride, to aid with farming and also for company.

Humans display considerable genetic variation

21st century fashion

Wool coat

Layered clothing appropriate for cold Montana nights

24th century fashion

Leggings common in women's fashion

Natural fibres

HUMAN FEMALE
KEIKO O'BRIEN

HUMAN MALE
ZEFRAM COCHRANE

EARLY SEAFARERS
Starfleet's officers are steeped in the traditions of Earth's earliest sea voyagers. Even as it explores the stars, Starfleet still follows many naval practices established on Earth centuries earlier.

A LEGACY OF EXPLORATION

From the earliest days of Earth's civilization, Humans have been explorers. They crossed deserts to settle new lands and took to the sea to discover the world beyond their shores. This natural curiosity inspired Humans to first journey into space in the mid-20th century. Hundreds of years later, they have developed starships that can fly further and faster than ever, and the invention of faster-than-light warp travel means they can explore new horizons far beyond the Sol System.

Titanium casing

Warp nacelle

Fuselage

Retractable nacelle pylon

Crew cabin (capacity: 1 pilot and 2 passengers)

Thrusters

First stage rocket engine

THE PHOENIX
Zefram Cochrane's ship, built from a Titan nuclear missile, is the first manned Earth ship capable of faster-than-light travel.

Plans for the *Phoenix*

HUMAN CULTURE

Humanity does not have a single culture; rather it is a combination of global societies that came together to form one United Earth. Through much of the planet's history, these separate civilizations were often in conflict with one another, culminating in the nuclear holocaust of World War III. By the 24th century a new, united civilization has risen from the ashes, in which Earth is no longer torn apart by war, or preoccupied with accumulating wealth. Humans now devote their time to bettering themselves through the peaceful study of science, art and a myriad of other subjects.

Commemorates Human inventor of warp drive

ZEFRAM COCHRANE STATUE

LITERATURE
The invention of the printing press in the 15th century allowed Humans to collect their stories and knowledge on the written page, and share them for centuries to come.

THEATRE
Acting is a part of Human culture even older than the written word. Human actors have played out tales for audiences on stages large and small since the days of Thespis, the first recorded actor, in Ancient Greece. Even in the 24th century Humans still pursue acting both as an occupation and a pastime.

SPORTS AND GAMES

Humans enjoy competition, and they often take pleasure in challenging themselves and testing the limits of their bodies through sporting activities. Competitive athletics first brought together nations in the Ancient Greek Olympic Games that originated in the 7th century BCE. For Humans, physical activity comes in many forms, and their ingenuity has produced a vast range of different sports, designed either for a single participant or multiple players, and involving different combinations of strength, speed, quick reactions and tactical planning.

Racquet (Max. width 56 centimetres/22 inches)

Racquetball court

Point targets

Serving stance

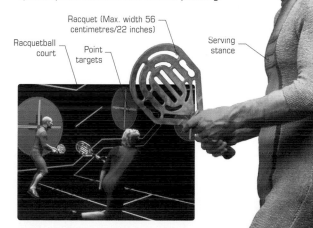

THE VULCANS

A RACE SEEN throughout the Galaxy as cold and unfeeling, Vulcans are actually a deeply passionate people. Left unchecked, their raw emotions resulted in a history of extreme violence until a leader named Surak ushered them into a new era, called the Time of Awakening. In the centuries since, Vulcans have followed Surak's teachings by learning to suppress their intense emotions in favour of logic and reason. Although initially reluctant to join with more impulsive races like Humans and Andorians, the Vulcans came to see the advantages of co-founding the United Federation of Planets.

VULCAN MALE
V'LAS

Upswept eyebrows

Pointed ears

Inner eyelid protects from the harsh sunlight

VULCAN FEMALE
T'LES

VULCAN
A hot and dry desert planet, Vulcan has a thin atmosphere, high gravity and extreme temperatures that make it inhospitable to many humanoid races. In spite of the harsh conditions, the planet boasts many religious and natural sites worthy of exploration. The temple at Mount Seleya, in the canyon known as Vulcan's Forge, is a particularly spiritual site.

Jewel represents the Vulcan sun

INIFINITE DIVERSITY
The teachings of Surak, the father of Vulcan philosophy, became the core of the Vulcan belief system. His theories are encapsulated in the Vulcan "IDIC" symbol, which stands for "Infinite Diversity in Infinite Combinations".

IDIC PENDANT

Hooded robe guards against the sun

VULCAN PHYSIOLOGY AND DRESS

Vulcans have adapted to life in a desert climate by developing a higher tolerance to the heat, a very fast heart rate and greater strength and reflexes than an average Human. However, their clothes are still designed with the warm temperatures in mind. Loose-fitting robes in lightweight fabric are designed for ease and comfort, and their colours often blend with the more natural shades of the desert, much like Vulcan architecture. Ceremonial wear tends toward bolder shades, often with deeper tones of reds and purples. Vulcan uniforms worn in off-planet travel have changed dramatically over the centuries, evolving from traditional robes to more practical form-fitting uniforms that allow for freedom of movement.

LIVE LONG AND PROSPER

The Vulcan salute is a gesture made by raising the right hand and separating the second and third fingers in a V-shape. The salute is traditionally accompanied with the phrase "Live Long And Prosper", a blessing that serves as both a greeting and a farewell.

VULCAN TECHNOLOGY

The Vulcans appear to have a simple lifestyle, but they were exploring the universe in warp-capable starships long before most other races, and are highly advanced in the fields of science and technology. The Vulcan Science Academy is the leading institution of higher education on the planet, and children train for years to gain acceptance to its hallowed halls. The Vulcans were once quite wary about sharing their knowledge with alien races, as it would have been illogical to place advanced technology in untrained hands, but they have grown more accommodating over time.

Impulse engines

Warp nacelle ring

CEREMONIAL SPEAR

Gold and jewelled spearhead

Scanning radius: 3 kilometres (1.8 miles)

Visual display

VULCAN SCANNER

Particle beam emitter

Ring folds into hull when powered down

D'KYR-TYPE COMBAT CRUISER 22ND CENTURY STARSHIP

2.5 metres (8 feet) tall

Synthetic string (ancient weapons were made from *sehlat* gut)

Upper limb

VULCAN CULTURAL ITEMS

Though they are one of the most technologically advanced races, Vulcan society remains steeped in the history and culture of their past. Ancient weaponry and ceremonial artefacts feature in their major rituals and still have a place in their daily lives. The reliance on these cultural relics serves as an ever-present reminder of how the Vulcan people have overcome their violent history in their search for enlightenment.

Tuning pins

Chord adjustment

Pitch alteration knob

LANGUAGE

The Vulcan language is incredibly complex, with multiple dialects. Family surnames are so intricate that they are almost impossible for non-Vulcans to pronounce. This is the reason most outsiders only know members of the race by their first names. The ornate written language is read in columns from top to bottom, and left to right.

LUTE

Hammered metal fins

BOW

VULCAN MARRIAGE

Vulcan parents choose their children's future mates at a young age, sealing the union in a ritual called the *Koon-ut-kal-if-fee*. Less than a wedding, but more than a betrothal, a telepathic bond is formed between the children that will drive them to reunite in adulthood, when they enter the mating time known as the *Pon farr*.

The *kal-if-fee* is a challenge to the marriage rite when one of the participants is unwilling to join in the union upon adulthood. The challenge is fulfilled through ritualistic battle using ancient weaponry, in which the woman can choose her champion or fight for herself.

Quiver with Vulcan script

Different symbols combine to create new words

Polyhedral dice

SYLLABIC CUBES

Symbols represent syllables in ancient tongue

VULCAN—HUMAN INTERACTION

VULCANS AND HUMANS have always been unlikely partners, with a mixed history of suspicion and respect. The Vulcans, having far greater experience in space travel and galactic politics, initially keep a tight rein on the more emotional race as they make their first tentative steps out into the stars. Through perseverance in the face of immense challenges, the Humans eventually convince their highly logical mentors that they are prepared to explore the stars, and finally come to be seen as equals.

Designed as both a science vessel and combat cruiser

Warp nacelle ring

Primary hull

Particle beam emitter

Tractor beam emitter

SURAK-CLASS CRUISER 22ND CENTURY STARSHIP

FIRST CONTACT
The first official interaction between Vulcans and Humans occurs on April 5, 2063 when the Vulcan survey ship, *T'Plana Hath*, detects the warp signature of Zefram Cochrane's first flight in his experiental craft, *Phoenix*. They deem the technological advancement this demonstrates makes Humans worthy of contact.

EARLY TENSIONS

Reluctant to aid Humans to explore beyond their solar system, the Vulcans attempt to delay the launch of Earth's first Warp 5-capable starship, *Enterprise* NX-01. The launch is finally forced to go ahead when an injured Klingon that has crashed on Earth has to be returned to his homeworld. The Vulcan High Command arrange to have a Vulcan observer, Subcommander T'Pol, assigned to Enterprise in exchange for the star charts necessary for the journey. Her presence on the ship is initially met with suspicion, but over time her interaction with the largely Human crew leads to a growing mutual respect.

SUBCOMMANDER T'POL

Vulcan duty uniform

FRICTION WITH EARTH
The terrorist bombing of the United Earth Embassy on Vulcan in 2154 is part of an intricate plot by the Vulcan High Command to provoke a war against the Andorians. When the plan is revealed, it leads to the dissolution of the High Command, and serves as a major step toward the formation of a unified interplanetary government, which will later evolve into the United Federation of Planets.

THE CARBON CREEK INCIDENT

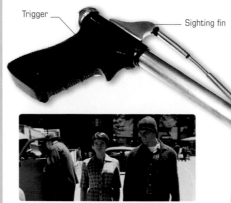

Trigger

Sighting fin

Although the official first contact between Humans and Vulcans does not occur until 2063, the Vulcans have Humanity under observation as early as the 1950s. At that time, a ship carrying T'Pol's great-grandmother and two other crewmembers crash-lands in the small Earth mining town of Carbon Creek, Pennsylvania. Before being rescued, the Vulcan crew try to minimize their contact with the Humans to avoid contaminating the pre-warp society, but are finally forced to use their advanced particle weapons in order to help rescue some trapped miners.

Particle emitter

PARTICLE WEAPON

Form-fitting fabric

VULCANS IN STARFLEET

Following the days of T'Pol serving as a crewmember on one of Starfleet's earliest vessels, Vulcans were heavily involved with the organization as it expanded to become the scientific and exploratory arm of the Federation. By the 23rd century it was still rare to find a Vulcan in the largely Human Starfleet crews, as they tended to segregate themselves from the more impulsive Humans for their own comfort. The *U.S.S. Intrepid* was one Starfleet vessel specially manned by a crew of 400 Vulcans in response to this concern. By the 24th century, Vulcans have become routinely blended into the crews of Starfleet vessels, and are now a common sight throughout the fleet.

SERVING IN UNIFORM
Unlike T'Pol, who initially served only as an observer in Captain Archer's Earth-based Starfleet crew, Vulcans now enlist as full members of Starfleet, enjoying rank and privilege befitting their positions. This includes the adoption of traditional Starfleet uniforms.

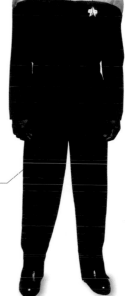

Combadge

Starfleet Operations uniform

24TH CENTURY STARFLEET UNIFORM

SPOCK STANDS TRIAL
One of the greatest testaments to the bond between Humans and Vulcans occurs when Spock, the first officer of the *U.S.S. Enterprise* NCC-1701, voluntarily stands alongside his Human crew to face court martial charges.

Pyramid shape represents Mt Seleya on Vulcan

RITUAL CANDLE
Spock's quarters on the *Enterprise* are full of traditional Vulcan artefacts, reminding him of his homeworld.

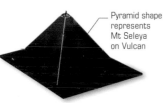

Vulcan greeting

IDIC pendant

Short, dark hair is traditional for Vulcans

Sciences Division uniform and insignia

Commander rank insignia

NERVE PINCH
Vulcans prefer to avoid physical violence unless completely necessary, and as serving in Starfleet can be dangerous, they use a number of non-violent defenses. Chief among these is to exert pressure to the nerve bundle at the base of the neck common to most humanoid species, immediately rendering the victim unconscious

MIND-MELD
Vulcan telepathic abilities have often proved useful on Starfleet missions. These include the power to read the thoughts of others through a "mind-meld" that bridges the consciousness of two individuals, allowing them to share thoughts.

SPOCK: HALF-HUMAN, HALF-VULCAN

The *U.S.S. Enterprise* NCC-1701's first officer, Spock, is one of the most notable Vulcans in Starfleet history. The son of Vulcan Ambassador Sarek and his Human wife, Amanda, Spock was estranged from his father for 18 years after choosing to join Starfleet instead of attending the Vulcan Science Academy. With a unique insight into both Human and Vulcan culture, Spock spends a large portion of his life aboard the *Enterprise*, even sacrificing himself to save the ship and his crewmates. However his *katra* (soul) survives his death, which allows Spock to be reborn in a ceremony on Vulcan. He eventually leaves Starfleet to serve as an ambassador, working to reunite the Vulcans with their Romulan cousins.

THE ANDORIANS

EASILY IDENTIFIED BY THEIR BLUE SKIN, silver hair and antennae, the Andorians hail from the icy moon of Andoria, which orbits the gas giant Andor. When the Andorians achieved warp drive travel they immediately struck out to find a more hospitable world in which to live. However, They quickly discovered that they were not alone in the Universe when they encountered the Vulcans, who lived in the neighbouring system. The Vulcans tried to contain the Andorians to their own star system, as they did with the Humans, though this move was met by a hostile reaction from this more volatile race.

Sight

Plasma emitter

Plasma generator

ANDORIAN PLASMA RIFLE

ANDORIANS AND THE FEDERATION

The birth of the United Federation of Planets owes much to the Andorians finding an ally in Humanity. Previous Andorian excursions into space were marred by their suspicions of the Vulcans and tensions with the Tellarites.

Though they did not become fast friends with Humans, these encounters were the first time that Andorians saw the potential for a partner in space exploration, paving the way for a unification of governments.

ARCH RIVALS: TELLARITES
A Romulan drone ship disguised as a Tellarite freighter brings years of tension between the Andorians and Tellarites to a head, when it destroys the Andorian battle cruiser *Kumari*. Full-scale war is only narrowly averted.

ANDORIA
The Andorians build their cities deep beneath the surface of their frigid planet, where they are kept warm by geothermal energy.

Severed antennae grow back in 9 months

Loss of antenna results in short-term disability

ANDORIAN MALE
THY'LEK SHRAN

Antennae aid in balance

Command sash

Ushaan-tor dueling weapon

Blue alcoholic beverage

AN ICY HISTORY

From the light blue skin on their bodies to the deep blue blood that flows through their veins, it is impossible to forget that Andorians come from a frozen world. That icy environment plays an important role in their history as many of their proudest accomplishments came from their ability to adapt to the harsh conditions of their home. Their grand tradition of ice mining continues to play an important role in their space-faring society, including the incorporation of the *Ushaan-tor* ice-miner tool into *Ushaan* duels. These honourable fights to the death follow a strict set of traditional rules, ending with the victor being toasted with a glass of Andorian ale.

ANDORIAN ALE

Stock

Available in silver or black

Trigger (weapon has no stun setting)

Large grip helps control recoil

TENSIONS WITH THE VULCANS

A hundred years of tenuous peace with the Vulcans grows more strained when Captain Archer of Earth reveals that the Vulcans are spying on the Andorians. The Human captain is later instrumental in negotiating a truce between the races.

Particle cannon

Warp nacelles

ANDORIAN WARSHIPS

Andorian vessels in the 22nd century are larger than their United Earth equivalents, like the NX-01. Despite this, they have relatively small crews of around 80 personnel. They are also heavily armed, and utilize advanced deflector shield technology.

Impulse engines

ANDORIAN TECHNOLOGY

The frozen environment of Andoria has played an important role in the planet's technological development, from the large-scale modification of planetary environmental factors (known on some worlds as "terraforming") to the use of plasma technology to break through the ice. Even the flagship of their 22nd century space-faring fleet, the *Kumari*, was named after the first ice cutter to circumnavigate the planet.

ANDORIAN BATTLE CRUISER
22ND CENTURY

Duranium alloy hull

THE IMPERIAL GUARD

Soldiers in the Imperial Guard proudly begin their training at a young age. It is considered a great honour to serve in the Guard, and its members are afforded elevated status in Andorian society. When a Guardsperson dies on duty off-planet, a comrade will take a piece of the deceased back to Andoria where it is added to the ice in the Wall of Heroes.

Movements can express emotion

Hair is white or silver

22nd century Imperial Guard uniform

ANDORIAN FEMALE
TALAS

Insulated material protects against cold

THE TELLARITES

OF ALL THE RACES that initially come together to form the Coalition of Planets, none is more outwardly emotional than the Tellarites. A belligerent race that has raised arguing to an art form, some consider them natural politicians. They open most negotiations with a complaint or – when failing to find anything worth criticizing – go straight for an insult. They are not entirely unreasonable, but it usually takes a cool-headed participant to engage them in any debate.

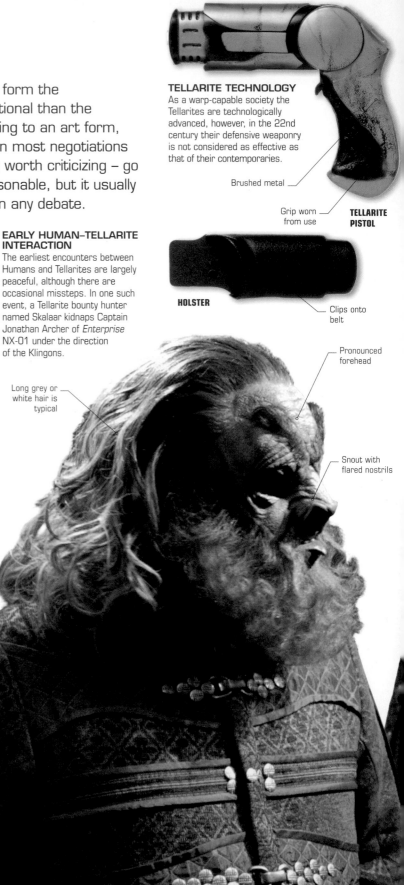

TELLARITE TECHNOLOGY
As a warp-capable society the Tellarites are technologically advanced, however, in the 22nd century their defensive weaponry is not considered as effective as that of their contemporaries.

Brushed metal

Grip worn from use

TELLARITE PISTOL

HOLSTER

Clips onto belt

Pronounced forehead

Long grey or white hair is typical

Snout with flared nostrils

EARLY HUMAN–TELLARITE INTERACTION

The earliest encounters between Humans and Tellarites are largely peaceful, although there are occasional missteps. In one such event, a Tellarite bounty hunter named Skalaar kidnaps Captain Jonathan Archer of *Enterprise* NX-01 under the direction of the Klingons.

DIPLOMATIC DISASTERS

As it is located in neutral space, the planet Babel often hosts Federation conferences. In 2267 one such meeting is nearly sabotaged when an Orion spy posing as an Andorian murders the Tellarite ambassador.

Vegetables are central to the Tellarite diet

TELLARITE FOOD

THE TELLARITE SPECIES

Tellarites are shorter and stouter than the average humanoid. They are a formidable people, possessing great physical strength, however they are not as adept as most humanoids, as their hands consist of only three fingers and bear a slight resemblance to hooves. Their diet is heavy on vegetables, but they are not exclusively vegetarian as some of them consider Earth canine to be a delicacy. Tellarites may be less technologically advanced than other space-faring species, but they have been exploring the stars for some time, pre-dating Humans in that field by several centuries.

Tellarite member of the Federation Council

TELLARITES IN THE FEDERATION

Bull-headed and argumentative, the Tellarites are not always the most pleasant race to be around, but they have been valued members of the Federation from its earliest days. A failed attempt by the Romulans to incite discord between the major races of the Alpha Quadrant in the 22nd century backfires, resulting in the first notable agreements between Humans, Vulcans, Andorians and Tellarites. That bond is instrumental in the ensuing Earth–Romulan war, in which the Tellarites are an important ally of Humanity. This early partnership forms one of the cornerstones of the Federation.

ANDORIAN–TELLARITE TRUCE
Once again, Humans are integral in bringing together warring factions of the Galaxy, with the negotiation of a truce between the Tellarites and Andorians following a long period of mutual distrust.

Deep-set eyes

Most Tellarite males are bearded

Upswept eyebrows

Thick skin

Heavy, textured garments

ENTERPRISE NX-01

THE *ENTERPRISE* NX-01 is the culmination of the programme to develop Earth's first engine capable of powering a starship for deep space exploration. Under the command of Captain Jonathan Archer, the son of the one of the lead scientists on the project, *Enterprise* is the initial starship in the NX-class and serves as Earth's first ambassador to the wider universe. *Enterprise*'s crew is responsible for many of the earliest interactions with alien beings that ultimately prove instrumental in the formation of the United Federation of Planets.

SICKBAY
Dr Phlox oversees the medical infirmary of the NX-01, combining his Denobulan medical knowledge with Earth's best healing technology to keep watch over *Enterprise*'s crew.

THE BRIDGE

The command hub of *Enterprise* NX-01 serves as the template that Starfleet ships will follow for centuries to come. The circular bridge centres on a lone command chair seated behind the helm and ringed by duty stations for security, engineering, sciences and communication. All focus on the bridge is directed toward the main viewscreen in the forward bulkhead. This allows for a real time look at the area of space in front of or surrounding the ship, as well as communication with individuals on other starships or planets.

Starboard navigation light

Cargo bay doors

Bridge

Navigational deflector

Registry number

Viewport

Reaction Control System (RCS) thrusters

Polarized hull plating

TRANSPORTER ROOM
Transporter technology allows for the near-instantaneous movement of people and materials via matter-energy conversion. Physical objects are briefly transformed into energy that is "beamed" to another location and then reassembled in its original form. Although the transporter is approved for biological use, the crew are initially reluctant to use the fledgling technology to transport themselves for fear of not being reassembled properly.

SITUATION ROOM
Located at the rear of the bridge, the command conference area provides the crew with a secure tactical centre in which they can discuss options for dealing with a crisis. Computers built into the walls and conference table provide up-to-the-minute information from sensor readings, communications and computer library information.

Nacelle pylon

Starboard warp nacelle

ARMOURY

Spatial and photonic torpedoes are stored and prepared for launch in the armoury. The fully automated system removes these weapons from storage and places them into torpedo tubes at the press of a button, saving the crew from the responsibility of manually preparing the highly volatile devices in times of crisis.

Symmetrical warp governor

Warp coils

Bussard collector

Impulse engines

THE NX-CLASS

United Earth's NX Project forms the core of the programme to develop a ship capable of carrying the Warp 5 engine. Several test vehicles are constructed in an attempt to perfect the design, but in spite of the success of an unauthorized test flight of the NX-Beta prototype, the Vulcans who are guiding the project insist on further study and analysis. Construction of *Enterprise* does not begin until after the development and flight of yet another test vehicle, NX-Delta. At the time of *Enterprise*'s launch in 2151, three other NX starships are in development, the next in line being the *Columbia* NX-02.

Port navigation light

Airlock

Roof airlock hatch

Polarized hull plating

Personnel hatches

Cockpit

Nuclear fusion engine pod

NX-01 ENTERPRISE   POD 1

SHIP OVERVIEW

- LENGTH: 225 metres (738 feet)
- DECKS: 7
- CREW: 83
- LAUNCH DATE: 2151

UNDERSIDE

STARBOARD ELEVATION

SHUTTLEPOD

The two shuttlepods on the NX-01 are used to ferry crewmembers to planet surfaces and other spacecraft. These are launched from a drop bay on the ship's underside. In spite of the small size of the interior cabin that seats a pilot and six passengers in cramped quarters, shuttlepods are often used in lieu of the transporters during the early days of *Enterprise*'s mission, due to fears about using the relatively untested transporter technology.

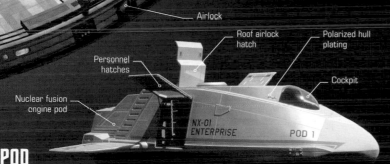

CAPTAIN ARCHER

**STARFLEET PATCH
UNITED EARTH,
C. 2151**

BORN IN upstate New York in the 22nd century, Jonathan Archer is the son of one of the lead scientists responsible for the development of the Warp 5 Engine. Archer's tenacity in the face of Vulcan delaying tactics enables his father's dream to become reality with the launch of *Enterprise* NX-01. As captain of *Enterprise*, Archer's personal leadership and accomplishments help form the Coalition of alien races that will become the Federation.

Starfleet regulations require tidy hairstyles

22nd century Command Division uniform

Enterprise mission patch

Captain rank pips

INTER-SPECIES RELATIONS

Captain Archer and his crew are responsible for much of the early contact with new alien civilizations. His extensive diplomatic skills combined with a bold attitude serve the captain well in navigating unpredictable situations, and turning potential enemies into allies.

Human

ARCHER'S CAREER

In spite of his occasional flagrant disregard for rules, Jonathan Archer has a distinguished Starfleet career. As captain of *Enterprise* he oversees the successful first contact with numerous alien races, defends Earth against scheming enemies, and brings together Humanity with the Vulcans, Andorians and Tellarites to form a new Coalition of Planets. Following his successful ten-year mission as captain of *Enterprise* he is promoted to admiral, and serves in a number of roles in the Federation government including Chief of Staff of Starfleet, Ambassador to Andoria, Federation Councilman and ultimately President of the United Federation of Planets.

Exterior lights

Oxygen tubing

Flame-retardent material

Environmental controls

Pockets maximize storage space

Hands left bare for dexterity

22ND CENTURY ENVIRONMENTAL SUITS

Environmental suits are worn for spacewalks or activities in any other inhospitable environments unfit for humanoid physiology. The suits are self-sealing so that in the event of a crack or tear, sealant automatically contains the breach to ensure that the wearer remains protected from depressurization.

ENTERPRISE: A HISTORY IN PICTURES

Captain Archer may be flying into the future on *Enterprise*, but his heart is deeply rooted in the past. His personal quarters are decorated with a number of items with historical significance, including a miniature version of the famed statue of space pioneer Zefram Cochrane in Bozeman, Montana and a 1960s National Aeronautics and Space Administration (NASA) ashtray. The walls of his ready room also display an artistic tribute to exploration, with pictures of some of the notable vessels throughout Earth history that also bore the name *Enterprise*. These images include the 18th century naval frigate, the 20th century aircraft carrier, the space shuttle, and the NX-01.

ARCHER AND THE VULCANS

Archer's interactions with new alien races often prove challenging, but nothing comes close to the frustration he experiences with the obstructive Vulcans. His relationship with the Vulcan people takes a more positive turn when he assists in the discovery of the *Kir'Shara*, one of their most important artefacts that contains the teachings of the philosopher Surak.

STARFLEET TECHNOLOGY

United Earth's Starfleet technology is perceived to be inferior to that of the Vulcans, but it is actually quite advanced and serves as a template for centuries to come. Communications technology advances greatly during the *Enterprise* crew's ten-year mission, particularly with the advent of universal translators that convert alien communication into the native language of the listener.

Antenna

Microphone

Interface

Transmits on
subspace frequency

COMMUNICATOR

Worn attached
to clothing

**UNIVERSAL TRANSLATOR
(ADVANCED)**

Beagle puppy

PORTHOS

Enterprise
artwork

Low ceiling requires
visitors to duck

Desk monitor

THE CAPTAIN'S READY ROOM

Captain Archer's ready room, located just off the bridge, serves as a personal office in which he can meet with members of the crew or visitors to the ship. It is also the home of his pet Beagle, named Porthos.

Communicator
slots into
translator

**UNIVERSAL TRANSLATOR
(EXPERIMENTAL)**

Translation
unit

CAPT. ARCHER'S CREW

THE PREMATURE LAUNCH of *Enterprise* leaves Captain Archer scrambling to assemble his crew, but the promise of deep space exploration and new alien interactions is more than enough to entice the team to come together. Over the course of their ten-year mission, the predominantly Human crew will grow close to their alien crewmates and form the kind of cohesive unit that will become standard in Starfleet for centuries to come.

HOSHI SATO

Hoshi Sato is a professor of exo-linguistics at a university in Brazil when Captain Archer uses a recording of the Klingon language to entice her to accept a commission aboard *Enterprise*. Sato has to persevere through some initial fears about the dangers of deep space exploration, but she quickly becomes a highly regarded member of the crew. Her work as communications officer is vital for the mission, as early versions of the universal translators are not always effective. She is also invaluable in furthering the study of exo-linguistics and the development of the universal translator.

Wireless receiver

COMMUNICATIONS EARPIECE

Plasma emitter

Rechargeable sarium microcells

Grip

PLASMA RIFLE

Life sign indicator

Collapsible display interface

SCANNER

Command Division uniform

Ensign rank pip

Sciences Division uniform

CHARLES "TRIP" TUCKER III

The self-taught chief engineer, Charles "Trip" Tucker, is a close friend to Captain Archer and co-conspirator in the theft and unauthorized test launch of the NX-Beta Warp 2 prototype vessel, in an attempt to prove the viability of its design to Starfleet. One of the first recruits for *Enterprise*, Tucker unofficially places himself in charge of morale by hosting a movie night for the crew. Over time he develops a close bond with T'Pol that blossoms into a romance.

TRAVIS MAYWEATHER

A "space boomer", born and raised on slow cargo ships not even capable of Warp 2, Ensign Travis Mayweather jumps at the chance to be *Enterprise*'s helmsman, piloting the fastest Earth ship in existence. Having already logged more time in space than most of his crewmates, Mayweather's tour of duty on *Enterprise* adds to his already impressive list of adventures – alongside Malcolm Reed he becomes one of the first two Humans to ever set foot on a comet.

22ND CENTURY MEDICAL EQUIPMENT

Starfleet medical equipment is the culmination of hundreds of years of technological advancement in the field of medicine on Earth, and offers capabilities unimaginable in earlier centuries.

Scanning array

Visual display

Simple controls

MEDICAL SCANNER

DR PHLOX

Dr Phlox is in the right place at the right time when Captain Archer is in need of a chief medical officer. The Denobulan doctor's treatment methods rely on a combination of modern technology and homeopathic cures that often include the healing properties of alien species, like the Altarian marsupial, whose droppings contain a regenerative enzyme.

Hypospray

MEDICAL EQUIPMENT

Protective animal transport

Altarian marsupial (in cage)

Placed on arm over vein

IV fluid

IV FLUID CUFF

T'POL

T'Pol is the first Vulcan to serve aboard a Human ship for an extended tour beyond two weeks. At first, the relationships between T'Pol and her crewmates are strained, but she quickly becomes absorbed into the Enterprise family. Her interactions with the crew help to change her opinion that Humans are too volatile for space travel, and accept that they can be trusted not only to explore the stars, but to serve as ambassadors to the wider Universe.

Vulcan duty uniform

Lieutenant rank pips

Operations Division uniform

Settings for stun and kill

Flip up cover

Trigger

PHASE PISTOL

This phase-modulated energy weapon fires a sustained beam or phase pulse. It has two settings: stun and kill.

Belt (attachable holster comes in matching material)

MALCOLM REED

Hailing from a family with a proud tradition of British naval officers, Malcolm Reed suffers from an intense fear of water that kept him from serving at sea, so instead he looked to the stars. Early in Reed's career he is approached to join Section 31, a covert organization inside Starfleet Intelligence. Reed does not remain with the group for long, but he is unable to permanently sever ties with the organization, which proves both problematic and beneficial during his time on *Enterprise*.

Edge of primary hull is
two decks thick

Viewport

Primary hull

U.S.S. ENTERPRISE NCC-1701

Phaser banks

Perimeter
sensor dome

THE 23RD CENTURY sees the first mission of a new
Enterprise, with the launch of the *USS Enterprise* NCC-1701.
Following many of the same design concepts as the NX-01,
with a saucer-shaped primary hull and twin propulsion
nacelles powered by a warp engine, this *Enterprise* is
capable of much faster Warp 9 travel. It can journey even
deeper into space to make contact with new life and new
civilizations, and the ship and its crew, under the leadership
of Captain James T. Kirk, become some of the greatest
representatives of Starfleet and the Federation in history.

ENGINEERING
The engineering department is responsible for
the care and maintenance of the ship's warp
engines. Most engine functions are controlled
from main engineering on Deck 19.

THE BRIDGE
Located on Deck 1 at the top of the primary
hull, the *Enterprise*'s bridge follows a similar
design to that of its NX predecessor from over
a century earlier. Captain Kirk leads his crew
from the elevated command chair, encircled by
command officer support stations. The bridge,
as on many ships in Starfleet at this time, is
a replaceable module that can be lifted out of
the ship as a piece and replaced during a refit,
to easily upgrade the ship's systems.

Navigational deflector/
Long-range sensor

RECREATION ROOM
The *Enterprise* has a recreation
room where the crew can go to
relax during off duty hours.

24

- LENGTH: 289 metres (948 feet)
- DECKS: 23
- CREW: 203 (min) 430 (max)
- LAUNCH DATE: 2245

Registry
number

THE CONSTITUTION-CLASS

The *Enterprise* is a *Constitution*-class vessel, named
after the *U.S.S. Constitution*, which was the first ship
in the line. They are also known as Class-1 Heavy Cruisers.
Designed as vessels of exploration, the experiences of
earlier craft like the NX-01 nevertheless mean that
these ships are heavily armed.
At the time of Captain Kirk's
original mission there are
12 *Constitution*-
class vessels
in Starfleet.

PRIMARY WEAPONS
The *Enterprise* is armed with a
dozen phaser banks strategically
located around the ship, which can
fire directed-energy beams at
enemy targets. Additional weapons
include six torpedo tubes that can
launch powerful photon torpedoes.

Warp nacelle

Warp
intercooler
intake

Control
reactors

Bussard
ramscoop

Nacelle pylon

Subspace field radiator

SHUTTLECRAFT
The *Galileo* Shuttlecraft is
the primary support craft
on the *Enterprise* until it
is destroyed on an away
mission, and replaced by the
Galileo II. Both vessels and
similar Class-F shuttles are
7 metres (24 feet) long, have
seating for seven, and are
powered by an ion engine.

THE REFIT
The *Enterprise* undergoes
several refits during its time
in service, but the most
comprehensive overhaul
follows Captain Kirk's initial
five-year mission. This refit
sees the installation of a
new bridge module and warp
nacelles, and upgrades to
every major system.

Engineering hull

Hangar deck

CAPTAIN KIRK

JAMES TIBERIUS KIRK is the third captain of the *U.S.S Enterprise* NCC-1701 but certainly the most famous. A decorated officer, Kirk embodies the adventurous spirit of Starfleet, willing to bend the rules when necessary, but only when in service of the greater good. In his days at Starfleet Academy Kirk was the only cadet to pass the infamous *Kobayashi Maru* "no-win" scenario test, which he did by reprogramming the simulation's computer. Though some might consider the action cheating, he earned a commendation for original thinking.

Human

KIRK'S SON
Kirk reunites with his estranged son, Dr David Marcus, in adulthood and reconciles their strained relationship, before David's untimely death at the hands of a Klingon commander.

LANDING PARTIES
Starfleet crewmembers are assigned to landing parties for planetary exploration. Though it is traditional for the captain to remain on the ship during these missions, Kirk often prefers to be in the thick of the action.

Antenna grid

COMMUNICATOR
Communicators are standard equipment for landing parties, providing a link between members of the team and the ship, and relaying the coordinates of the device to the ship's transporter.

Speaker

Microphone

Type-3 phaser

23rd century Command Division uniform

A STARFLEET LEGEND
Kirk has a varied and sometimes troubled career. Following his initial five-year mission on the *Enterprise* he is promoted to admiral and becomes chief of starfleet operations. Never one to be far from the action, he temporarily steps down and again takes command of the *Enterprise* to deal with an alien threat to Earth. Twelve years later, Kirk steals the *Enterprise* in a desperate attempt to save his first officer's life. The ship is destroyed in the process and his actions are seen as a court martial offence. However, between the theft and his trial he successfully saves Earth from yet another hostile entity, which is taken into consideration in the court's judgment. He is demoted to captain and given command of the newly-built *U.S.S. Enterprise*-A.

Admiral rank pin

Startleet insignia pin

ADMIRAL'S UNIFORM

23RD CENTURY ENVIRONMENTAL SUITS
Less streamlined but more robust than earlier examples, 23rd century environmental suits are worn in any hostile environment, such as ships that have suffered a hull breach.

Intercom

Programmable controls

Shuttlecraft hangar deck controls

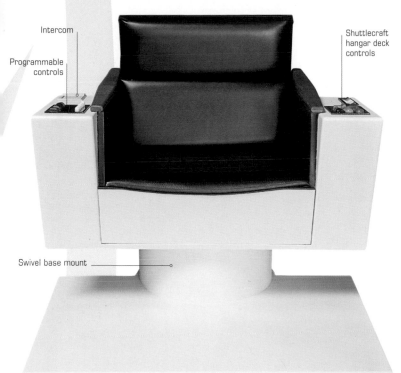

Swivel base mount

Following over a century of tensions, in 2293 Kirk is instrumental in enabling the Federation and the Klingons to move beyond old prejudices and sign the Khitomer Peace Accords, uniting two of the major powers in the Galaxy.

CAPTAIN'S COMMAND CHAIR

From his raised command chair, Kirk can have face-to-face meetings with captains on other ships via the main viewer, monitor the bridge crew around him and communicate with the rest of the ship through the communications panel in the armrest.

Upper movable attack board

Primary board

Lower movable attack board

OUT OF UNIFORM

Captain Kirk may be a dedicated officer, but that never stops him from having fun in his downtime. A known ladies' man, Kirk has dated women both in and out of Starfleet, although he is unsuccessful at building any long-term relationships, possibly because the *Enterprise* has always had his heart. The captain is a playful man, who enjoys a good joke or a wry comment, often at the expense of his highly logical first officer. More than anything, Kirk is a true and loyal leader who is there for his crew, the Federation and its allies – and sometimes even its enemies.

TRIDIMENSIONAL CHESS

Captain Kirk and Commander Spock are skilled players at Tridimensional Chess – an evolved version of traditional Chess. The officers can often be found leaning over a board in the recreation room when off-duty.

TRIDIMENSIONAL CHESS SET

64 squares spread over multiple levels

Piece storage

CHESS PIECES

HOME AWAY FROM STARSHIP

After his promotion to admiral, James Kirk lives in a San Francisco high-rise near Starfleet Command. The apartment is large and spacious, but it can never compare to Kirk's cramped quarters aboard a starship, which will forever be his true home.

CAPT. KIRK'S CREW

LIKE ON SO MANY Starfleet ships, the personnel on the *Enterprise* are more like family than crewmates. They have been there for one another throughout their two five-year missions and beyond. They put their careers on the line to save the life of Spock when he sacrifices himself to save them, and stand together when charged with the infractions they commit in the process. The *Enterprise*'s crew are steadfastly loyal to each other and their beloved captain no matter where they are stationed. This is true in any century ... and they have visited a few.

MEDICAL TRICORDER
A portable medical tricorder is a diagnostic tool that can perform a full physical examination, analyze the information gathered, and provide an update on a patient's condition. It is a Starfleet doctor's primary tool used both in the sickbay and on landing party missions.

Hypospray

STARFLEET MEDICAL KIT

HYPOSPRAY
The hypospray relies on a high-pressure aerosuspension delivery system for medication, replacing hypodermic needles.

Applicator

Medicine vial

MEDICAL SCANNER
The wireless hand scanner works in conjunction with the tricorder to perform localized examinations.

CREW INTEGRATION
Spock likes to practise on his Vulcan lute in the recreation room, where Uhura often joins him in song.

DR LEONARD "BONES" MCCOY

The chief medical officer of the *Enterprise* thinks of himself more as an old country doctor rather than the highest-ranking medical professional aboard a starship. The cantankerous McCoy is still reluctant to use the transporter in spite of over a century's worth of technological development for the device. Like his captain, McCoy is quick with a joke, especially at Spock's expense, but he gets down to business quickly when the situation calls for it.

Tricorder strap

Sciences Division uniform

SPOCK

The ship's half-Vulcan science officer usually finds himself on the receiving end of jokes about his unemotional attitude, but he more than holds his own with his dry observations. As he was raised on Vulcan, Spock's time with the *Enterprise* crew has taught him much about his Human half, but nothing has been more important than the lesson that the needs of the many do not always have to outweigh the needs of the few.

Monitor

Library disks

MONTGOMERY "SCOTTY" SCOTT

The *Enterprise*'s chief engineer is a bit of a miracle-worker, able to conduct repairs in half the time it would take the average Starfleet engineer. With the possible exception of the captain, no one could love the *Enterprise* more than Mr Scott.

Operations Division uniform

Operations patch

TRICORDER
Tricorders have medical, scientific and engineering applications. They are used to collect sensor data and analyze the information.

Type-1 phaser integrated into type-2 design

Emitter

Receiver

NYOTA UHURA

As communications officer aboard the *Enterprise* it is Uhura who first makes contact with most alien races. On regular duty she monitors subspace transmissions for emergency beacons or any other forms of communication, often alerting the crew to coming danger. Beyond her technical skills, she is also a talented singer who has been known to serenade her crew in the recreation room. The name Uhura is derived from the Swahili word for "freedom".

Trigger

TYPE-2 PHASER
This Phased Energy Rectification weapon comes with a variety of settings for various levels of stun, heat and beam width.

UHURA'S EARPIECE

HIKARU SULU AND PAVEL CHEKOV

Helm officer Sulu and navigator Chekov are responsible for defending the *Enterprise* and guiding it through space. These two members of the crew excel at their mission, rising through the ranks and taking positions on other ships, but never travelling too far from their home on *Enterprise*. Chekov returns to the *Enterprise* following a stint as first officer on the *Reliant*, but Sulu eventually accepts his own command aboard the *Excelsior*.

WEAPONS EXPERT
Sulu has a personal interest in antique Earth weapons, and is also a skilled fencer.

Targeting scanner

Lieutenant rank

Uhura is usually the first to hear incoming messages

U.S.S. ENTERPRISE NCC-1701-D

THE 24TH CENTURY *U.S.S. Enterprise* NCC-1701-D is the sixth Starfleet ship to bear the proud name. The *Enterprise*-D is the flagship of the Federation, and boasts many distinctive design features. These include a detachable saucer section, classrooms and family quarters as the exploratory vessel for the first time also provides a home to the spouses and children of its crew. Under the leadership of Captain Jean-Luc Picard, the *Enterprise*-D has taken part in recorded first contact meetings with many notable alien races including the Ferengi, the Q Continuum and the Borg.

Primary hull (saucer section)

Ten-Forward Lounge

Sensor strip

Ventral phaser array

Registry number

Captain's yacht (docked)

TEN-FORWARD LOUNGE
Located, fittingly enough, on Deck 10 in the forward part of the saucer section, Ten-Forward provides a relaxed informal space for crew recreation, and is also a popular music venue. Guinan, the El-Aurian bartender, is a particularly skilled listener to any concerns that crewmembers might have.

THE MAIN BRIDGE
The *Enterprise*-D's bridge has a more relaxed feel than its predecessors. The captain's chair, positioned behind the conn and operations consoles, is the centremost of a trio of seats on an equal level. The first officer sits to the captain's right while an additional seat for a command crewmember (often the ship's counsellor) is to the left of the captain. A tactical station is incorporated into the railing above the captain's chair while engineering and science consoles line the rear bulkhead to allow complete control of the ship from the main bridge.

Cabin access door

Forward viewport

SHUTTLECRAFT
Shuttlecraft on the *Enterprise*-D can be found in three shuttlebays on the ship. They are generally used for lengthy excursions or any trip outside transporter range. The *Enterprise* carries several shuttle designs including the Type-6 Shuttlecraft and Type-15 Shuttlepod.

CONTROL CONSOLS
Touch-screen consoles are located throughout the ship that interface directly with the Library Computer Access and Retrieval System (LCARS).

Warp nacelle

Phaser array

TYPE-6 SHUTTLECRAFT

SAUCER SEPARATION

The *Enterprise*-D is primarily on a peaceful mission of exploration, but the universe can be a dangerous place. In an emergency, the saucer section can decouple from the engineering hull, splitting the *Enterprise* into two separate ships. The engineering hull then takes a lead role in a battle, protecting the saucer section.

AFT ¾ ELEVATION

STARBOARD ELEVATION

- LENGTH: 641 metres (2,103 feet)
- DECKS: 42
- CREW: 1014 (typical)
- LAUNCH DATE: 2347

THE GALAXY CLASS

Galaxy-class vessels share the familiar basic design of most Federation starships throughout history, although they are far larger than their predecessors, and are among the most advanced ships in service. Since they are designed to carry families along with the crew, the saucer separation feature is especially valuable. It enables civilians and non-Starfleet personnel to be evacuated to the saucer section in emergencies to protect them from the dangers of battle.

Impulse engines

Transporter emitter

Photon torpedo launcher

Vehicle separation plane

Secondary phaser array

Port warp nacelle

Engineering hull

Main deflector

Tractor beam emitters

Nacelle pylon

THE HOLODECK
The holographic environment simulator creates true-to-life characters and environments for a fully immersive virtual reality experience. The holodeck is used for both training and recreation.

ENGINEERING

The engineering department is the beating heart of the ship. The warp core contains a matter-antimatter reaction that provides power to the nacelles, enabling the ship to achieve the faster-than-light speeds necessary for deep space travel. In an extreme emergency, such as a core breach, the warp core can be ejected. This effectively leaves the ship dead in space, only able to maintain slow impulse power.

CAPTAIN PICARD

JEAN-LUC PICARD could not resist the siren song of the stars and, against his father's wishes, left his family vineyard in France for Starfleet at age 18. As a cadet, Picard achieved high honours, however his time at the Academy was marred by a serious rules infraction, and soon after graduation a cocky display of attitude put his life in jeopardy. Having learned his lessons, Picard goes on to have a long and distinguished career, going above and beyond the call of duty on numerous occasions.

Captain rank pips

Starfleet insignia combadge

PICARD'S READY ROOM
Located off the main bridge, Picard's ready room is the office in which he meets with individuals of his crew, visitors to the ship and alien dignitaries. He can often be found relaxing in there on his downtime by reading, or enjoying a cup of tea (Earl Grey, hot).

Telescope

Horizon mirror

Scale

PICARD'S ANTIQUE SEXTANT

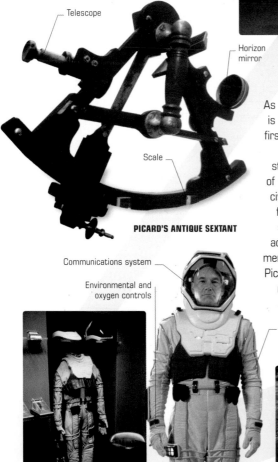

PICARD AND THE PRIME DIRECTIVE

As captain of the Starfleet flagship, Picard is often assigned diplomatic missions and first contact meetings. Like most captains of his generation, Picard also tries to strictly follow Starfleet's Prime Directive of noninterference with alien cultures and civilizations. This order prohibits officers from influencing the development of alien societies, particularly those that have not yet achieved warp travel, which is a prerequisite for membership in the Federation. At the same time, Picard is aware that the Directive is not a perfect rule and has, at times, grappled with the moral consequences of the order.

Communications system

Environmental and oxygen controls

Insulating material protects wearer from extreme temperatures

24th century Starfleet Command uniform

24TH CENTURY ENVIRONMENTAL SUITS
The design of the 24th century environmental suit features an advanced customized fit for a specific wearer.

Magnetic boots for walking on exterior hull

BOOTHBY
Picard still credits the irascible Starfleet Academy groundskeeper, Boothby, with helping him graduate due to the advice the older man once gave him as a cadet. The long-lived gardener still remembers Picard decades later as he tends to the school grounds, counselling the cadets and warning them to stay out of his flowerbeds.

PERSONAL ITEMS

He may captain one of the most advanced ships in the fleet, but Jean-Luc Picard is intrigued by the past. He is a keen amateur archeologist who enjoys the study of ancient civilizations and the search for artefacts and other items of historical significance.

Artefact from the extinct planet of Kataan

RESSIKAN FLUTE

Smaller statues rest inside the hollow shell

KURLAN "NAISKOS" STATUE
Picard's former mentor, Professor Galen, uses this rare statue from the Kurlan civilization in an attempt to entice the captain to join him on a hunt for an ancient humanoid race.

Picard is fascinated by the 1930s "Dixon Hill" detective series

DETECTIVE NOVEL

DIXON HILL'S
THE BIG GOODBYE
by Tracy Tormé

Vineyard logo

CHATEAU PICARD
Picard keeps bottles of red wine from his family vineyard in La Barre, France.

Touch-sensitive monitor

Connects wirelessly to the ship's LCARS computer system

GALAXY CLASS STARSHIP

USS ENTERPRISE • NCC-1701D

Power button

Blade is touched to forehead to signify mourning

DATHON'S DAGGER
This dagger was a gift from the Tamarian, Dathon, to commemorate him and Picard finding a way to communicate without the use of traditional language.

CAPTAIN'S DESK MONITOR

PICARD AND THE BORG

The darkest period in Picard's life occurs when he is abducted by the Borg Collective, who place cybernetic implants into his body, transforming him into "Locutus of Borg". The Borg then use Picard's knowledge of Starfleet tactics to destroy a Federation fleet at the Battle of Wolf 359, resulting in the loss of 11,000 lives. Picard is subsequently rescued and the cybernetic implants removed, but the memories continue to haunt him.

CULTURAL AMBASSADOR
Picard's diplomatic skills earn him a place on a number of ambassadorial missions including Ambassador Spock's attempt to reunite the Vulcans and Romulans. He is also one of the few Federation captains to take part in time-honoured Klingon rituals, often at the request of his Klingon security officer, Worf.

THE CAPTAIN'S QUARTERS

Like his ready room, Picard's personal quarters are decorated with ancient artefacts and his favourite books. It is a place where he can get away from his problems, unless they follow him there, as happened when he woke to find the mischievous alien, Q, in his bed.

PICARD'S ARTIFICIAL HEART

As a brash young ensign fresh out of the Academy, Picard instigated a bar fight with a trio of Nausicaans and was stabbed from behind. The wound would have been fatal if not for a cardiac replacement procedure in which he received an artificial heart. Picard learned a lot about himself following the incident and has sought a more measured and diplomatic response to conflict ever since.

Wound caused by Nausicaan knife

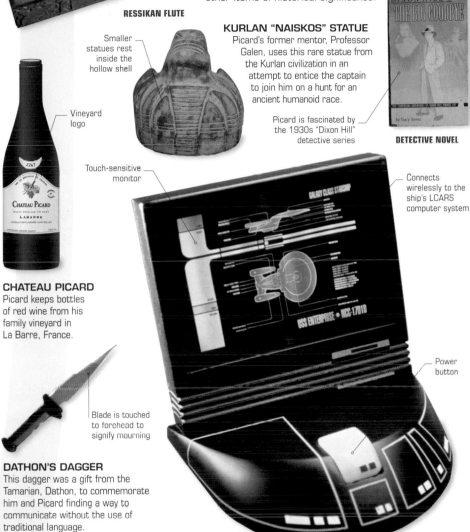

CAPT. PICARD'S CREW

THE CREW of the *Enterprise*-D has experienced a lot together, from the loss of a crewmate to the marriage of their first officer and counsellor. They are among the most elite of Starfleet crews, but they still find time to have fun together on the holodeck or enjoy the occasional game of poker.

DEANNA TROI

Deanna Troi is a calming presence as she serves in her role as ship's counsellor. Being half-Betazoid, Troi relies on her empathic powers to assist her crewmates with their troubles. This ability is also useful when dealing with unknown alien threats.

WILLIAM RIKER

William Riker is second-in-command of the *Enterprise*-D, responsible for personnel issues and leading away missions unless the captain deems his own presence necessary. Riker is a decorated officer who is reluctant to leave the *Enterprise* even when pressured to assume his own command. Eventually, he goes on to captain the *U.S.S. Titan* with his new wife, Deanna Troi, though he still maintains close relationships with his former captain and crew.

Commander rank pips

Combadge

Carried when weapons must be inconspicuous

Power level indicator

Trigger

Emitter

TYPE-1 PHASER

Emitter

Trigger

Beam intensity control

Grip

TYPE-2 PHASER

Non-uniform makes Troi more approachable and less formal to the crew

Traditional Klingon baldric

Type-2 phaser

Identifies Worf as "Champion Standing"

WORF

Worf is the first Klingon in Starfleet, originally serving as conn officer on the *Enterprise*-D before being promoted to chief of security following the death of crewmate Natasha Yar. Orphaned as a child, Worf was adopted and raised by Human parents, but he remains deeply respectful of his Klingon heritage and, as an adult, tries to honour both of his families as best as he can.

BAT'LETH TOURNAMENT TROPHY

COMMUNICATOR BADGE

In the 24th century, hand-held communicators have been replaced by personal combadges in the shape of the Starfleet insignia, which are magnetically attached to the uniform. A simple tap on the communicator allows the wearer to make contact with the ship or other crewmembers.

DATA

The first and only sentient android to serve in Starfleet, Data was created by Dr Noonien Soong as a near-perfect replica of a Human, except for the fact that he was not built to experience emotion. Consequently, Data aspires to improve on his programming and become as Human as possible by studying concepts like humour, friendship and even dance. He also adopts a pet cat, whom he names Spot.

Synthetic skin

Tricorder

Lieutenant commander rank pips

Orange tabby

SPOT

PADD
The Personal Access Display Device is a handheld interface capable of connecting with a ship's computer.

Comm transmission

Display screen

Emergency upload

Applicator

MEDICAL TR-580 TRICORDER (OPEN POSITION)

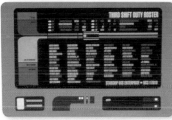

Medicine vial

MEDICAL EQUIPMENT
The Enterprise is equipped with the most advanced medical equipment available to Starfleet in the 24th century. Even so, the main tools of the profession – the hypospray and medical tricorder – are based on technology initially developed two centuries earlier.

HYPOSPRAY

GEORDI LA FORGE

As the child of Starfleet officers, La Forge moved often in his youth, finding life to be a great adventure. He began his career on the Enterprise-D at the conn, but was quickly promoted to chief engineer. Born sightless, La Forge wears a bioelectric Visual Instrument and Sensory Organ Replacement (VISOR) that allows him to see much of the electromagnetic spectrum. Eventually, his VISOR will be replaced by ocular implants with similar abilities.

Sensors

Neural implant connector

GEORDI'S VISOR

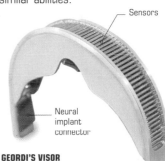

Commander rank pips

Medical tricorder

DR BEVERLY CRUSHER

The chief medical officer aboard the Enterprise has known the captain for many years thanks to the fact that her late husband, Jack, was a close friend to Picard. Dr Crusher's bond with the captain has evolved on its own since her husband's death, at times coming close to a more personal relationship. Her son, Wesley, is considered an engineering savant, and is briefly posted on the Enterprise-D as acting ensign.

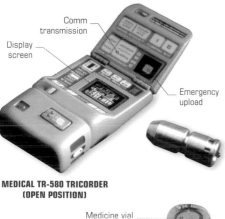

THE BETAZOIDS

Telapathic ability develops in the paracortex of the brain

Betazoid irises are completely black

THE RESIDENTS of the planet Betazed are a race of telepaths, which makes them particularly skilled diplomats since they can read the minds of those with whom they are negotiating. Betazoids traditionally acquire their telepathic abilities in adolescence, though some are born already able to access them. This often results in particularly skilled telepaths, though there is also a risk of mental instability because they are unable to filter out the thoughts of others. Traditionally, Betazoids learn to do this at an early age out of respect for the private thoughts of others.

BETAZED

Betazed is a tranquil planet filled with lush gardens, crystal blue lakes, and flowing waterfalls. It also boasts one of the most advanced institutes of higher learning in the Federation with the University of Betazed. The planet, however, experiences one of its darkest periods in the 24th century when it is briefly occupied by the Dominion during the Federation–Dominion war.

Outfits match bold personality

DEANNA TROI: HALF-BETAZOID

Because Deanna Troi is half-Human, she does not have full access to her telepathic powers and is merely an empath, able to sense the emotions of others.

Primarily communicates through sign language

Arms of superior strength to a Human's

AMBASSADOR LWAXANA TROI

Lwaxana Troi is daughter of the Fifth House of Betazed, Holder of the Sacred Chalice of Rixx, Heir to the Holy Rings of Betazed, and mother to *Enterprise*-D counsellor, Deanna Troi. Lwaxana is a larger-than-life character who takes her diplomatic role seriously, but never lets that stop her from having fun. The widowed Federation ambassador sees no reason to filter her words when she can read other people's thoughts, and she always shakes things up when she visits the *Enterprise*-D along with her valet, Mr Homn.

Uttaberries

MR HOMN

THE DENOBULANS

THE 12 BILLION inhabitants of the planet Denobula all live on one continent where living space is at a premium, forcing them to adopt a communal, close-knit society. Denobulans are polyamorous with each adult taking three spouses, which leads to very large extended families. Although the Denobulans were active partners in the early days of the first Coalition of Planets, they have since withdrawn and have not been major players in galactic politics.

Facial ridges

High hairline

Enlarged, bisected brow

Eye colour changes with mood

DENOBULAN MEDICAL SHIP

EXOBIOLOGY

Denobulan participation in the Vulcan-initiated Interspecies Medical Exchange helps them develop a better understanding of the physiological differences between alien races.

Tongue extends several centimetres

Denobulan tongue scraper

Smile wider than an average Human's

Face can puff out when threatened

DENOBULAN TONGUE

DENOBULAN FACIAL STRUCTURE

DENOBULAN PHYSIOLOGY

Humanoid in design, the Denobulan body is nevertheless different from a Human's in several key ways. The most distinctive features are a pair of ridges that frame the face and a longer ridgeline that extends down the back. Denobulan faces are also remarkably pliable and their toenails grow so rapidly that they need to be groomed at least once a week.

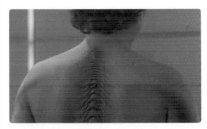

DR PHLOX

Dr Phlox is over 80 years old at the time he joins the crew of the *Enterprise* NX-01, which is still considered young for a Denobulan. He has three wives with five children between them. Those wives, in turn, each have three husbands of their own. All told, there are a total of 31 children in Phlox's extended family and about 720 familial relationships overall. Phlox's children are all grown by the time he accepts his commission on *Enterprise*, building lives and new relationships of their own.

Three-quarter length jackets are typical Denobulan fashion

THE TRILL

TRILL ARE A UNIQUE RACE, as certain members of their society are chosen to host a symbiont being. This parasitic entity merges with the Trill, bonding two individuals in one body. The host body has an average humanoid lifespan, but the symbiont is considerably longer-lived, moving through several host bodies. The symbiont is the dominant personality, though both symbiont and host retain their individual personalities. Once joined, the symbiont's name also becomes the new entity's last name.

THE MANY LIVES OF DAX

The Dax symbiont has lived many interesting lives, in both male and female host bodies. When Jadzia Dax is placed under the command of Ben Sisko on *Deep Space 9*, it is a reunion of sorts as Sisko had known Dax's previous host, Curzon. Curzon's memories transferred to Jadzia with the Dax symbiont, just as her own experiences will be shared with Dax's next host, Ezri, following Jadzia's death.

TRILL HOMEWORLD
The Trill homeworld is a Class-M planet, and is home to both the Trill and the symbionts. The humanoid Trill live on the planet's surface while the symbionts reside within interconnected pools in the underground Caves of Mak'ala. Outside of the pools, symbionts can live only in their hosts or else they will die.

Trill spots run the length of the body

JADZIA DAX

Tri-octave keys

Easily portable

Trill script

24th century swimwear

Beach covering

TRILL CULTURAL ITEMS
The combination of Trill that live relatively short lives and symbionts that exist for centuries has resulted in a technologically advanced society that retains deep ties to its past.

TRILL KEYBOARD

TRILL MEDICAL TRICORDER

Design mimics Trill spots

Pivoted blades

Symbionts live in an abdominal pocket

TRADITIONAL SHEARS

THE JOINING

In the Joining, a symbiont is placed within an abdominal pocket of the host body. The host and symbiont soon become biologically interdependent and within 93 hours neither can survive without the other.

SYMBIONT

THE EL-AURIANS

EL-AURIANS ARE ANOTHER long-lived race in which a single lifespan can last for several centuries. There are very few El-Aurians left in the Universe since the Borg attacked their homeworld and devastated their race. The few that remain live largely nomadic lives, scattered throughout the Galaxy. They have a reputation for being good listeners, but tend towards the cryptic when speaking. Some are also suspected to be sensitive to shifts in the time-space continuum.

GUINAN
Guinan, the bartender and operator of Ten-Forward Lounge on the *Enterprise*-D, is a valued member of the crew, often providing sage counsel to her crewmates.

External appearance similar to Humans

Considered good listeners

DR TOLIAN SORAN

Following the loss of his family and the destruction of the El-Aurian homeworld, Tolian Soran grows obsessed with entering the Nexus. This is an extradimensional realm where reality can be rewritten, allowing him to forget his pain. His single-minded pursuit of this goal destroys stars and costs many lives, as he tries to gain access to a spatial anomaly that acts as a gateway to the Nexus.

Probe

Trilithium

Control panel

SOLAR PROBE
Soran's launch device is capable of firing a probe carrying trilithium into a star, which will then create a chain reaction causing it to implode. The resulting shift in gravity will send the passing spatial anomaly to collide with the planet Veridian III, where Soran will be waiting.

Guidance fins

Launch platform

Style geared to long robes or gowns

EL-AURIAN REFUGEES

Following the destruction of their planet, El-Aurian refugees on two ships en route to Earth encounter the spatial anomaly attached to the Nexus. The anomaly destroys both ships, but the *U.S.S. Enterprise*-B is able to rescue 47 of the refugees, including Guinan and Dr Soran.

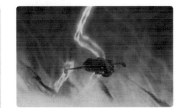

THE ENERGY RIBBON
The entrance to the Nexus is a powerful spatial anomaly that passes through the Galaxy every 39.1 years.

ARTIFICIAL INTELLIGENCE

AS COMPUTERS HAVE BECOME ever more powerful, the definition of intelligent life has become increasingly blurred. There are those who argue that if a being is intelligent and self-aware, then it is a sentient life-form with all the rights that entails, however others assert that such awareness is merely a simulation, regardless of how lifelike it seems.

Skull composed of cortenide and duranium

Bioplast sheeting for skin

B-4's head held in framework for analysis

NOMAD

Launched from Earth in 2002, the *Nomad* space probe was one of the earliest Human-built space vehicles with a computer capable of independent thought. *Nomad* was sent into space to search out new life-forms, but collided with an alien probe on its own mission to gather and sterilize soil samples. The two programs merged and *Nomad* became convinced that its job was to sterilize imperfect life-forms. The crew of the *U.S.S. Enterprise* NCC-1701 encounter *Nomad* over 200 years after its launch and are forced to destroy what has become a sentient killing machine.

Acquisition sensor

Computer databanks

Selective amplifier screen

Primary power system

NOMAD MK-15C

SOONG-TYPE ANDROIDS

"Soong-Type Android" is a term that defines a handful of artificial humanoid life-forms designed and developed by famed cyberneticist Dr Noonien Soong. These highly advanced "robots" possess a positronic brain rendering them capable of independent thought and action, with intelligence equal to the most advanced computers of the 24th century. Several models of android have been created, including B-4 and Lore, but the pinnacle of the design type is Data: a fully functional artificial life-form who becomes the first android member of Starfleet to serve on a starship and achieve the rank of lieutenant commander.

**B-4
EARLY SOONG
PROTOTYPE**

Diagnostic device

DATA'S ART
Data spends much of his life trying to improve on his programming by learning to appreciate the interests of Humans and other organic life-forms.

Data's painting of his pet cat, Spot

EMOTION CHIP
Initially incapable of feeling emotions, Data is later gifted with feelings by his creator in the form of an emotion chip, which is briefly stolen by his "brother", Lore.

DATA'S EMOTION CHIP

DR NOONIEN SOONG
A descendent of disgraced geneticist Arik Soong, Dr Noonien Soong was himself initially ridiculed when his early work on a positronic brain suffered from high-profile failures. The scientist went into hiding, but continued working with his wife, Juliana, and perfected his creation of completely life-like androids. Soong's most convincing android is a replica of his wife that he created after she fell into a coma.

EXOCOMP

What began as an experiment in servomechanics to create an advanced tool for engineering work resulted in the potential for a new artificial life-form. Created by the Tyran scientist, Dr Farallon, the initial Exocomp prototypes were built to serve as an adaptive tool system that anticipates the needs of a repair situation and then creates the proper solution. The Exocomp technology is so advanced that it begins to reprogram itself, first revealing a hint of sentience when, in an act of self-preservation, one of the Exocomps refuses to seal a dangerous plasma conduit.

TECHNICAL SPECS
An advanced microreplication system allows Exocomps to create any tool, making them fully capable of addressing any engineering need. This, combined with evolving circuitry, leads to the potential for sentient thought and action.

Tool attachment

Command module

EMH Mark 1 has appearance of its creator, Dr Zimmerman

HOLOGRAMS

Holographic life-forms are three-dimensional projections of light and sound, often simulating humanoid appearance. The ability to create a magnetic containment field in which the electromagnetic energy can be trapped allows these manifestations of light to take a solid form, and manipulate objects just as any humanoid with flesh and bone can. Advanced computer technology can, at times, make them appear self-aware and even lead to a state of awareness approaching sentience.

EMERGENCY MEDICAL HOLOGRAM
The Starfleet Emergency Medical Hologram (Mark 1) was developed by Dr. Lewis Zimmerman as a short-term supplement to the doctors aboard Federation starships. As the medical staff aboard the *U.S.S. Voyager* are killed when the ship is pulled into the Delta Quadrant, the ship's EMH is left as the only available Starfleet medical professional. Over time, "the doctor" works to expand his programming, aided by the acquisition of a mobile emitter that allows him to move beyond rooms equipped with holographic projectors.

Hologram of Countess Regina Barthalomew

Professor James Moriarty

PROFESSOR MORIARTY
One of the first known sentient holograms, Professor Moriarty is based on a fictional character from the Sherlock Holmes detective stories. The holographic Moriarty grows out of a request for the *U.S.S. Enterprise*-D holodeck computer to create a character with the ability to outwit the android, Data. This results in a highly advanced hologram with the ability to learn, which eventually develops consciousness.

Holographic representation of Earth clothing c. 1887

Moriarty program trapped inside

HOLODECK MEMORY MODULE

HD25 ISOMORPHIC PROJECTION
Developed on the planet Seros in the Delta Quadrant, HD25 Projections are tasked with extreme hazard clearance on starships. The *U.S.S. Voyager* encounters one such projection, Dejaren, which has become unstable and murdered its abusive crew.

ALLIED SPECIES

AS THE FEDERATION'S BORDERS have expanded, many species that share its ideals have petitioned to become members. Among these are the Bolians and Benzites. These allies have become integrated into the Federation's institutions, including by serving in Starfleet.

Both male and female Bolians are typically bald

Cartilaginous lining on tongue

Heart on right side of chest

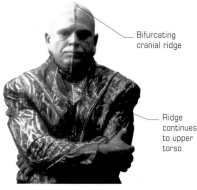

Bifurcating cranial ridge

Ridge continues to upper torso

BOLIAN FASHION
Bolians tend to adorn themselves in bold designs to match their gregarious personalities. It can often be difficult to tell the difference between the casual clothes of a shopkeeper and the official outfit of an ambassador.

THE BOLIANS

The residents of the planet Bolarus IX are distinguished members of the Federation, active in all levels of Starfleet. They are well known for their generally positive disposition and comprise one of the fastest growing alien communities on Earth. Like Andorians, Bolians are not only blue-skinned, their blood is blue as well — the chemical makeup of that blood is structurally different from many other humanoid races, making transfusions difficult, if not deadly. Bolians are also capable of consuming foods that are highly acidic or even spoiled, meaning that other races often find Bolian cuisine disagreeable.

SERVICE PROVIDERS
Bolians, like Humans, engage in many different passions in life, and take on diverse roles in society. Onboard the *Enterprise*-D, they fill traditional crew roles, along with service positions including ship's barber and waiting-staff.

Facial tendrils

THE BENZITES

The meticulous Benzites hail from the planet Benzar, which does not become a full member of the United Federation of Planets until the 24th century. The first Benzite to attend Starfleet Academy joins in 2364, while officer exchange programmes between Benzar and the Federation also take place at that time to foster a better understanding between alien races. Benzites have several unique features that make them stand out from other humanoid species, the most prominent being the possession of two opposable thumbs on each hand. Non-Benzites find that individuals from the same *geostructure* (the Benzite term for a city) appear identical.

breathing apparatus

Chemical controls

BOLIAN FEMALE

RESPIRATION DEVICES
The atmosphere on Benzar is different to that of most traditional Class-M planets, which initially forces Benzites to wear respirators when breathing in environments with an oxygen/nitrogen atmosphere. Advances in Benzite medical technology render the respiration device obsolete by the year 2372.

NON-HUMANOIDS

ALTHOUGH HUMANOID LIFE-FORMS dominate the Galaxy, not all beings follow that pattern. The scale and diversity of the universe means that strange new species are constantly being discovered, from ancient races like the Horta, to ecological nightmares such as the Tribbles.

Shell composed of silicone and trace elements

HORTA EGGS

Once every 50,000 years, the entire Horta race dies out, except for a lone survivor that is left to care for the collected eggs of her people. That Horta becomes mother to a new race of children and will do anything to protect the eggs if they are threatened, including killing anyone that does the offspring harm.

THE HORTA

In spite of her unusual appearance, the Horta is a sentient being that possesses an indeterminate level of intelligence. She is able to communicate with humanoids in a limited fashion by melting written languages into stone, or via a Vulcan mind-meld. This silicone-based life-form is a subterranean dweller that produces a strong corrosive acid, which is deadly to Humans, but allows her to tunnel through solid rock. When the Federation first comes into contact with the Horta, there is only one in existence, in spite of the fact that the race enjoys an unusually long life-span almost entirely unmatched in the universe.

Secretes corrosive acid

Silicon-based life-form

Skin impervious to type-1 phasers

Feeds on rocks

JANUS IV

Federation mining personnel on the Horta's home planet of Janus IV accidentally destroy numerous Horta eggs. They are horrified when their terrible mistake is revealed.

THE TRIBBLES

They may not be intelligent beings, but few living creatures have had the kind of impact on spacefaring races than that of the adorably destructive Tribble. A hermaphroditic species, Tribbles are born pregnant and reproduce at an accelerated speed. A single Tribble can produce an extremely large number of offspring in only a short amount of time – around ten an hour – posing all kinds of problems on a cramped starship. Sold as pets by unscrupulous individuals in the 23rd century, the Tribble species is believed to be extinct a century later, until the crew of the U.S.S. Defiant accidentally travel into the past, and on their return reintroduce them to the population of Deep Space 9.

Newborn Tribbles grow very rapidly

Tribbles come in a variety of colours

THE ENTERPRISE INFESTATION

In 2267 Lieutenant Uhura of the U.S.S. Enterprise receives a Tribble as a gift. When she brings it onboard the creature quickly multiplies and its offspring threaten to overrun the ship. In the process, the Tribbles uncover a plot by a Klingon operative when they consume a shipment of poisoned grain, and Captain Kirk discovers them dead.

THE FERENGI ALLIANCE

MOST ALPHA QUADRANT RACES established their place in the universe through the development of warp drive engines, but the Ferengi made their mark by simply purchasing the technology. The Ferengi are defined by their greed, and were unusually hostile during the first official contact between their people and the Federation. Although tensions quickly eased between the powers, as of the latter part of the 24th century the Ferengi Alliance is still not a member of the Federation.

THE ROSWELL INCIDENT
A sabotaged shuttlecraft leads to the first unofficial contact between Ferengi and Humans, when a trio of hapless Ferengi from *Deep Space 9* are flung back in time to Roswell, New Mexico on Earth in 1947.

Four-lobed brain

Extremely sensitive ear lobes

Sharp teeth to intimidate trade partners

FERENGINAR
The homeworld of the Ferengi is most notable for its humid climate, which comes as a result of nearly year-round precipitation. Because of this, the Ferengi language has approximately 178 different words for "rain".

THE GRAND NAGUS
The Grand Nagus serves as master of commerce to the Ferengi Alliance. He alone holds sway over the most important deals among his people, often setting (and changing) the terms of business as he sees fit. The cane of the Grand Nagus is a sign of his authority, and his people kiss the gold-plated head of the cane when in his presence.

Blue fingernails

A SOCIETY RULED BY PROFIT

Contrary to the Federation, which has largely moved beyond any interest in the accumulation of wealth, the Ferengi Alliance is motivated primarily by profit. The government has evolved to maximize commerce among its people, ruthlessly enforcing capitalism by forming a body of laws that benefit the average businessman, and rarely protect his customers or workers. Their society strictly follows the business philosophies of the Rules of Acquisition, which were first set down 10,000 years earlier by Grand Nagus Gint.

COMMERCE AUTHORITY SEAL
The Ferengi Commerce Authority (FCA) is charged with the oversight of business transactions and trade laws.

FCA SEAL

Tailored clothes signify commercial success

**FERENGI MALE
QUARK**

Rule #1: "Once you have their money, never give it back".

Made from cheapest possible materials

THE RULES OF ACQUISITION BOOK

Ferengi script

Gold casing

Liquid latinum inside

STRIP OF GOLD-PRESSED LATINUM

GOLD-PRESSED LATINUM
The Ferengi monetary unit is broken down in value from the smallest to the largest by the slip, strip, bar and brick. Each consists of a comparatively worthless gold outer-casing containing valuable liquid latinum.

Firearms are often used as trade goods in Ferengi business deals

Plasma generator contained in grip

Trigger

Emitter

PHASER

The Ferengi phaser comes in a multitude of styles and colours, making it part dangerous weapon and part valued collectible.

HOSTILE TAKEOVERS

The Ferengi are largely a peaceful race, more concerned with commerce than conflict. There are, however, factions of the Ferengi that have been prone to violence, especially in the early days of Federation–Ferengi relations. Though the Ferengi possess much in the way of advanced weapons technology, the bulk of it has been obtained through trade rather than by invention.

Torpedo launcher

Extendable neck

Energy weapon

Bridge

D'KORA-CLASS MARAUDER

VACUUM-DESSICATED REMAINS

FERENGI DEATH RITUAL

The Ferengi death ritual is characteristically profit-driven. Vacuum dessiccation is used to reduce the deceased's body into a powder-like material, which is then placed in a set of 52 disks. These are marked with the Ferengi Seal of Dismemberment to confirm their authenticity, and then sold as collectibles on the Ferengi Futures Exchange.

FERENGI MARAUDER

The Marauder is the most powerful ship design in the Ferengi fleet. Classified as both a transport ship and an attack vessel, it can fire a plasma energy burst strong enough to disable a Federation *Galaxy*-class starship.

Proper ear maintenance is integral to Ferengi grooming

High-speed grinder

TOOTH SHARPENER

Power cell

EAR HAIR COMB AND MIRROR

KEEPING UP APPEARANCES

As natural businessmen, Ferengi are always concerned with conveying the proper impression of success, and strive to be the snazziest dressers around. This also translates to their personal grooming skills. With the Ferengi ear being so prominent, proper maintenance of that body part is key, especially as a Ferengi grows older. Another key feature is properly sharpened teeth, which are maintained through powered grinding devices… or with a wooden chewstick at a pinch.

FEMALES IN FERENGI SOCIETY

Female's ears smaller than male's

Wearing clothing is a new trend among Ferengi women

Ferengi are a male-dominated society with oppressive views on the role of women. Females are forbidden to work in business or own property, and are not even permitted to wear clothing. Though the Ferengi Alliance has been taking small steps toward allowing greater freedom for women by the late 24th century, it has been met with resistance from conservative males, in spite of the Grand Nagus's support.

THE XINDI

Slit-like pupils

Ridgeline
typical of all
Xindi species

"Suicide gland"
releases
neurotoxin if
captured

XINDI-REPTILIAN BIORIFLE

Power cell is
an eel-like
organism

Contains
biomechanical
engineering

THE XINDI ORIGINALLY HAILED from the planet Xindus, a world located in a treacherous area of space known as the Delphic Expanse. Six different species of sentient beings evolved on Xindus, each with unique physical characteristics and personalities, but similar DNA profiles. By the 22nd century only five of those species have survived: Aquatics, Arboreals, Insectoids, Primates and Reptilians. The sixth species, Avians, were destroyed in a civil war between the races. The five surviving species settled on different planets in the Expanse and attempted to unite under a single government.

XINDI SUPERWEAPONS

XINDI PARTICLE WEAPON PROBE

The Xindi launch an attack on Earth in 2153, based on falsified information from a race of time-travellers indicating that Humans will be responsible for the death of the Xindi four centuries in the future. A Xindi probe armed with a particle weapon carves a path of destruction from Florida to Venezuela, killing over 7 million people.

Using technical data taken from the probe, the Xindi continue to work together to develop a technology powerful enough to destroy the entire planet. The final weapon requires activation codes from three of the races to ensure that no single Xindi can arm the weapon alone.

XINDI SUPERWEAPON TYPE 3 PROTOTYPE

THE XINDI COUNCIL

The Xindi Council is made up of representatives of the five surviving races of Xindi. Its formation came at the behest of a group of extra-dimensional, time-travelling beings known as The Guardians, who become gods to the Xindi. The Council members are often at odds with one another, and the group finally dissolves when some of them start to question the Guardians' lies about Humanity, after several encounters with the crew of the *Enterprise* NX-01.

XINDI-ARBOREAL

XINDI-PRIMATE

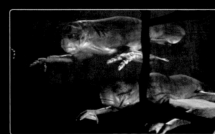

SPECIES DIFFERENCES
The various Xindi races may share DNA, but their physiological needs can be vastly different. The Aquatics, for instance, require large pools of water to live as they must remain submerged for survival, while the Reptilians are cold-blooded.

XINDI-REPTILIAN

Number of belts indicates rank

THE SULIBAN

THE SULIBAN ARE A NOMADIC RACE, spread through the Galaxy after their homeworld became uninhabitable around the time of Earth's 19th century. Most Suliban found a new home in the Tandar Sector where they live a largely peaceful existence. Physically speaking, they are comparable to Humans in strength and endurance and are generally considered unthreatening. However, in the 22nd century a faction of Suliban breaks off as a terrorist cell taking guidance from a mysterious figure from the future.

FUTURE GUIDANCE
The Suliban Cabal's benefactor from the 28th century offers them genetic enhancements, which allow them to achieve previously impossible feats. The goal is to enlist them as fighters in a Temporal Cold War between several time-travelling species out to change history.

ENHANCED TECHNOLOGY
The Suliban also receive advanced technology and weapons from the future for their actions in the Temporal Cold War. Spherical Cell Ships are single-person fighters equipped with particle weapons and cloaking devices to mask them from sensors. These small vessels can unite to form a larger, more powerful starship in a helix design.

CELL SHIP

Viewport

Emitter

Trigger

Mottled design matches Suliban appearance

SULIBAN PISTOL

Biomimetic clothing

Artificially enhanced senses

Pistol

THE SULIBAN CABAL

As galactic terrorists, the Suliban Cabal take orders from their mentor from the future who bribes them with gifts of genetic enhancements in exchange for their work in the Temporal Cold War. This faction of a previously peaceful race is responsible for attacks on Humans, Klingons and the Tandarans, among others. Their leader, Silik, is the main contact to their mysterious benefactor, and he interferes with the crew of *Enterprise* NX-01 on several occasions. Disenchanted by the mysterious voice from the future, a splinter group eventually breaks off from the Cabal, forming a resistance movement.

Silik, leader of the Cabal

GENETIC ENHANCEMENTS
The Cabal's genetic alterations are discovered by the crew of *Enterprise* during an autopsy of a dead terrorist. The enhancements give Cabal members extraordinary abilities beyond anything other members of their species can perform. Chief among these gifts is a shape-shifting ability that allows them to compress their bodies into a form so thin that they can slip under doors. Enhanced senses and strengthened bodies allow them to survive even in the most extreme environments.

Shape-shifting abilities

THE TALOSIANS

A RACE BROUGHT TO THE EDGE of extinction by nuclear war, the Talosians now inhabit underground caves on their planet, Talos IV. Having lost the ability to work the advanced technology of their ancestors, Talosians find entertainment by mentally creating illusions in the minds of others. Led by a figure known as The Keeper, They have become addicted to the fictional lives they view, and capture unwary visitors to their planet to use as new sources of imagery. Ultimately, they plan to use these prisoners to repopulate their world.

Pulsating membrane

TALOSIAN MALE
THE KEEPER

Bodies have atrophied from lack of use

Enlarged brains

Use telepathic communication

TALOS IV

Thousands of years after the nuclear war that nearly wiped out the advanced Talosian civilization, there is little evidence of the species that calls the planet home. However, its surface is once again able to support life.

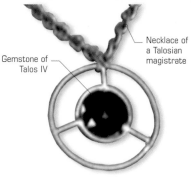

Gemstone of Talos IV

Necklace of a Talosian magistrate

THE KEEPER'S PENDANT

MIND GAMES

Talosians can create intricate illusions with fully immersive environments, replicating anything from simple memories to entire alien worlds. They are so convincing that their subjects can become trapped, unable to separate the dream world from reality.

FEDERATION INTERACTION

The Talosians have had minimal contact with the Federation over the centuries. Their most notable meetings occur in the 23rd century, when on two separate occasions Federation personnel are taken prisoner by the Talosians in an ill-advised attempt to repopulate their world. As a result of these incidents Starfleet General Order 7 is established, making it a violation to visit the planet because of the risk of entrapment in the Talosian's illusions. In spite of that rule, the *U.S.S. Enterprise* later returns to the planet on an unapproved humanitarian mission.

THE ORIONS

HAILING FROM THE PLANET ORION, this alien race tries to maintain a neutral relationship with the Federation. This is beneficial for most Orions because their way of life does not always fit within the regulations of "civilized" societies. Outwardly, their culture seems to be built on slavery, especially the forced enslavement of women. However, a little known truth is that the Orion "slave" women are actually in control, ruling over a race that engages in large-scale criminal enterprises.

THE ORION SYNDICATE

The Orion Syndicate is one of the most formidable criminal organizations in the Galaxy, with a reach that extends throughout the Alpha and Beta Quadrants. Engaging in blackmail, extortion, slave trading, piracy and assassination, by the 2370s the syndicate has expanded to incorporate numerous alien races into its organization, although the membership fee is high and its rules are applied with deadly force.

ORION WOMEN
Female Orions emit a pheromone that makes them extremely attractive to most male humanoids. That pheromone, along with their natural powers of seduction, can entrap men, turning hapless slave owners into virtual slaves themselves.

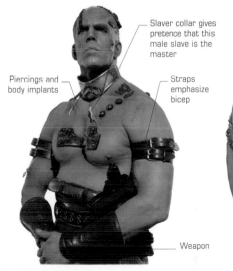

Slaver collar gives pretence that this male slave is the master

Piercings and body implants

Straps emphasize bicep

Weapon

ORION CLOTHING
Orion women wear minimal clothing to enhance their seductive prowess, while men's apparel is often intended to enhance their powerful bodies, which are generally more muscular than a Human's.

SLAVER SHIPS
Orion ships are equipped to capture other humanoids for the purpose of enslavement. A strong towing cable can be used to ensnare vessels while they abduct the crew.

Green skin emits potent pheromone

Long dark hair is the "classic" Orion look

Moves with animalistic grace

Expensive, revealing clothing encourages "slave" purchase

THE THOLIAN WEB

Chief among Tholian offensive weapons is an energy field based on tractor technology, used to ensnare ships in an impenetrable "web". A minimum of two Tholian vessels are required to "weave" the energy web around a starship while they remain outside weapons range. Once the energy field is complete it will close in on the victim ship until it is destroyed.

THE THOLIANS

THE THOLIAN ASSEMBLY, the planetary government for the Tholians, may have established diplomatic relations with the Federation by the 24th century, but it is a tenuous relationship marred by several centuries of aggression from the Tholians. The Tholians have long been considered a xenophobic species with an aggressive approach to territorial disputes. They have actively engaged with Starfleet personnel in a number of conflicts; enough that the organization has prepared battle scenarios specifically to deal with the unique threat presented by Tholian technology.

THOLIAN PHYSIOLOGY

Tholian bodies are insectoid in appearance, having segmented torsos with two arms and six legs. They tend toward russet colouring with glowing points at the top of the upper torso, which are possibly the source of the radiation they can control and use for personal communication. They prefer ambient temperatures in excess of 200 degrees Celsius and, further distinguishing them from humanoids, their body has an outer shell that is mostly mineral in composition. The Tholians are actually a race of hermaphrodites, with each individual belonging to both genders.

THOLIAN STARSHIPS

Tholian starships tend to be smaller than most Federation vessels, but their technology more than makes up for the size difference. Their ships are armed with weapons comparable to Starfleet plasma torpedoes, but their main technology is their web energy field.

THE DEFIANT INCIDENT

On a search and rescue mission in Tholian space, the *U.S.S. Enterprise* NCC-1701 finds the Federation starship *Defiant* adrift with all aboard dead. Unknown to Kirk, the *Defiant* has become trapped in a spatial anomaly between universes, leading to emotional instability among the crew that has caused them to kill each other. Captain Kirk becomes trapped on the derelict ship, lost in "interspace" as his crew come under siege from the Tholians.

Emits potentially radioactive glow

Faceted head and torso

THOLIAN LANGUAGE

Tholian speech consists of sequences of sharp clicks and squeals, which makes it difficult for a universal translator to process. The Tholians' obsession with punctuality often makes ship-to-ship communication a tense experience for Starfleet personnel.

THE GORN

THE GORN, UNDER THE LEADERSHIP of their governing body, the Gorn Hegemony, are a mostly neutral warp-capable power based in the Beta Quadrant. They can be quick to act aggressively when they feel under threat, which can sometimes lead to violent misunderstandings as it did in the 23rd century, when conflict marred their first contact with the Federation. By the 24th century, relations have become more cordial as most tensions have been resolved and the Gorn have allied with the Federation, though they have not sought official membership in the organization.

FIRST CONTACT
First contact between the Federation and the Gorn occurred under extreme duress due to a territorial dispute that turned violent. The Gorn attacked Federation settlers on Cestus III, killing most of the colony under the mistaken belief that their presence on the planet was an intentional incursion into Gorn space.

THE GORN CAPTAIN
Gorn ships follow a command structure similar to that of Starfleet, with a single captain in leadership of a starship roughly similar in speed and power to a *Constitution*-class vessel.

Makeshift weapon

Large, multi-faceted eyes

Inset ear

Razor-sharp teeth

Thick scales

Claws

GORN PHYSIOLOGY

The Gorn are a reptilian race that are comparable to humanoids, being a four-limbed bipedal species. Beyond that, the races' physiologies begin to diverge. Like Earth reptiles, the Gorn are cold-blooded, preferring warm climates. Their skin is scaly and tough, giving them an overall more durable physical form than that of most Humans. They also tend to be many times stronger than Humans, though slower and not nearly as agile. Although they can be quick to use violence, the Gorn do appreciate sound reasoning and are an intelligent species.

Captain's uniform

THE METRON CONNECTION
Captain James T. Kirk of the *U.S.S. Enterprise* NCC-1701 is the first known Human to personally engage in combat with a Gorn. A mysterious and powerful alien race known as the Metrons force Kirk and a Gorn captain to engage in a fight to the death, in order to resolve the dispute over Cestus III.

Crushing strength

FORCED COMBAT
In battle, both Kirk and the Gorn show resourcefulness in adapting weapons from their surroundings. Kirk's agility and ingenuity make up for a lack of power compared to his opponent, and he eventually uses a primitive cannon to fell the Gorn. When Kirk gains the upper hand, however, he refuses to kill the Gorn having come to realize their dispute is better resolved through diplomacy.

ALIEN THREATS

Although the beauty of the Galaxy can be beguiling, danger can come in many forms. There are predatory life-forms that seek to feed on the unwary, and countless aggressive and devious alien species that enjoy attacking the weak or stealing from the helpless.

Horn

Spike ridge along spine

Can reach over 2 metres (6.5 feet) in height

Venomous teeth

Claws for gripping prey

Covered in thick fur

THE MUGATO

This carnivorous species is native to the planet Neural, where a primitive tribe known as the Hill People reside as a protectorate of the Federation. Although this ape-like beast is not an intelligent creature, it is a notable presence on the world, feared for its violent behaviour and the lethal poison it possesses. The Mugato attack method is to force its prey onto the ground whereupon it will bite its victim to inject a deadly venom. As no known anti-toxin exists within Starfleet medical archives, the only cure for the poison must be created by a local medicine woman known as a *Kuhn-ut-tu*, using a native plant named *Mahko* Root.

MUGATO TRACKS
The footprints of the Mugato are easily identified, and are greatly feared by the Hill People of Neural.

THE NAUSICAANS

Nausicaans are a violent race with an almost complete disregard for Federation laws. They are quick to anger and enjoy games that inflict pain on one another. Nausicaans often hire themselves out as mercenaries or provide muscle for the highest bidder, regularly serving as enforcers for the Orion Syndicate. In the 24th century, a trio of Nausicaans is responsible for a near-deadly attack on the recent Starfleet Academy graduate Jean-Luc Picard, who will later captain the *U.S.S. Enterprise*-D.

Energy generator

Trigger

NAUSICAAN DISRUPTOR PISTOL

Double-barrelled pistol

NAUSICAAN WEAPONS
Nausicaans prefer bladed hand-to-hand weapons for close contact assaults and are skilled combatants, though they rarely fight fair. They also have a well-developed arsenal of handheld directed energy weapons as well as impressively armed ships.

PIRATES
Though they are not as organized as the Orions, Nausicaan pirates make coordinated attacks against transport vessels from as early as the 22nd century.

Pistol capable of firing a single or double beam

THE M-113 CREATURE

This predatory creature was the last remaining humanoid on an otherwise uninhabited planet. In the 23rd century the Federation knew little about this world, which was catalogued as M-113, and were even less familiar with the life-form that dwelt there. The creature had the ability to hypnotize its victims by seemingly taking on other peoples' appearances. Once a victim was under its spell, the creature would drain all the salt from their body, which was necessary for its survival. The life-form's true name or the history of its people has never been discovered.

SALT EXTRACTION
The M-113 creature's hands bear growths like suction cups that can drain the salt from its victims. Sometimes, the painful process can break the victim from its hypnotic spell.

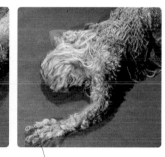

EXTINCTION
The creature attempted to prey on Captain Kirk, however once the illusory spell was broken during the attack, his screams of pain alerted Dr McCoy to the situation. Regretfully, the creature had to be killed by a phaser blast to save the captain's life.

Creature's true appearance becomes apparent as hypnosis fades

Although extremely dangerous, the M-113 creature was a highly intelligent life-form

Larger than average ears for a humanoid

Wrinkled skin

Small eyes

Hands have four fingers

Yridian yak leather bindings

THE YRIDIANS

Like Nausicaans, Yridians are primarily known for their mercenary ways, though they are not as predictably violent. Yridians are primarily dealers of information, willing to sell out anyone for a lucrative deal. They do not generally care if their information leads to the death of another and are not above committing murder themselves. Although they have a reputation as an untrustworthy society, that does not prevent their fine beverages such as Yridian tea and brandy from being enjoyed throughout the Alpha and Beta Quadrants.

THE BREEN

A DUPLICITOUS AND ENIGMATIC RACE, the Breen Confederacy has, at times, been an outright enemy of the Federation. With hearts as cold as the planet they hail from, the Breen have been responsible for a number of vicious attacks on other powers, forcing prisoners of war to work as slaves in their dilithium mines and torturing them for information. The Breen are also not above betraying an ally if the proper circumstances present themselves, which is why the Romulans have a saying that, "You should never turn your back on the Breen."

ATTACK ON EARTH
The Breen launch a surprise attack on Starfleet Headquarters in San Francisco, on Earth in the year 2375. The act marks their entry into the Dominion War. Many lives are lost in the attack that devastates parts of the city, but Starfleet forces combined with the existing planetary defenses are able to destroy most of the attacking force.

24TH CENTURY BREEN WARSHIP
Breen warships are distinctively asymmetrical, and their advanced technology makes them formidable vessels when in combat.

Deflector dish

Torpedo launchers

Energy-dampening weapon

Incorporates organic technology

REFRIGERATION SUITS

The Federation knows little about the Breen, and even less about their homeworld beyond the fact that it is a frozen wasteland, where temperatures drop so low that icy Andoria would feel mild in comparison. The frigid climate is rumoured to be the reason Breen have no blood or other liquid circulatory systems. When they travel off-world, Breen require refrigeration suits to maintain their low body temperature. Because of these suits, few people in the Federation even know what a Breen looks like.

Sensor enhanced visor

Heavily-insulated refrigeration suit

ENERGY-DAMPENING WEAPON
Similar in concept to an electromagnetic pulse (EMP), the Breen energy-dampening weapon can drain power from enemy ships, effectively leaving them adrift and helpless, and easily destroyed.

DOMINION ALLIANCE
The Breen join with the Dominion in their war against the Federation in the 24th century. This alliance shifts the war in the Dominion's favour thanks to the advanced technology possessed by the Breen. However it also marginalizes the Dominion's Cardassian allies – a fatal error for the Dominion

THE Q

THE Q ARE a race of extra-dimensional beings with skills far beyond that of a typical humanoid. These nearly omnipotent, possibly immortal beings claim to have always existed, yet it is unclear how they came to be or the process by which they evolved into all-powerful life-forms. They can manipulate time, space and the destiny of entire races. With their limitless abilities, many of the Q possess the kind of arrogance that makes them believe they have the right to judge and condemn "lesser" species.

Can assume any form, but typically appears as a humanoid male

Q often wears clothing from Humanity's past

Able to teleport

Earth judicial robe *c.* 2079, designed to intimidate

JUDGE OF HUMANITY

The single member of the Q that has had the most interaction with the Federation is their representative, Q. As all members of the society bear the "name" Q, it is often difficult to distinguish them from one another in discussion. This particular Q first makes his race's presence known when he comes aboard the *U.S.S. Enterprise*-D to place its captain and crew on trial for the perceived crimes of Humanity. Much of what Q does is inexplicable, and his judgment ends with a delayed verdict, as he chooses to study Humans further. This brings him into contact with Starfleet many more times through the latter part of the 24th century.

THE Q CONTINUUM
The Q inhabit an extra-dimensional plane known as The Q Continuum. Like the Q themselves, this space can assume any form, as it does on the occasions the crew of the *U.S.S. Voyager* visit it. Each time, the Continuum adopts a visual interpretation that can be easily understood by Humans, such as a run-down shack on a desert highway, or a battle from the American Civil War.

PICARD'S TORMENT
Although Q has also visited Starfleet Captains Sisko and Janeway, it is the captain of the *Enterprise*-D, Jean-Luc Picard, who has logged the most visits from the irascible being. These meetings generally begin with Q intending to teach Humanity a lesson, but over time it has become clear that Picard has had a greater impact in educating Q.

THE KLINGON EMPIRE

KLINGON EMBLEM

D'k tahg blade

Sagittal crest (forehead ridges)

Three lungs – extra organs increase resiliancy in battle

The Klingons have a long, violent history, and value honour above all else. Unlike the Vulcans who have turned away from their brutal past, the Klingons have embraced their heritage, incorporating its noble savagery into every aspect of their society. In spite of this aggressive tendency, they are an immensely proud race with a grand warrior tradition ... and a bit of underhanded treachery mixed in.

Fur from a targ (a boar-like animal native to Qo'noS)

QO'NOS

Qo'noS (pronounced Kronos) is the Klingon homeworld, located at the heart of the Empire and serving as its capital. An ecological disaster caused the destruction of the planet's moon, Praxis, in the latter part of the 23rd century, which severely damaged Qo'noS's ozone layer.

Knife of the House of Duras

24th century uniform

KLINGON SOCIETY

Klingon society has developed around their proud warrior tradition. The Empire is ruled in a psuedo-feudalistic manner, with power based on noble Great Houses. Members of these houses are united under a family crest, worn proudly on a baldric across the torso, and the houses themselves have joined together in a single government led by a Chancellor. However, they are often in conflict with one another and, on occasion, have used deceit to usurp power. Rituals, traditions and above all, family reputation form the cornerstone of Klingon laws, and are used to ensure that power remains in the rightful hands.

THE AUGMENT VIRUS

Klingons encountered by Starfleet in the 23rd century were often missing their forehead ridges

One of the darkest periods in Klingon history occurred in the 22nd century, when geneticists attempting to produce advanced warriors created a virus with the potential to drive their race into extinction. A cure was found, but the effects of the disease were seen for decades, most notably in the loss of forehead ridges among the infected.

KLINGON MALE
CHANCELLOR GOWRON

KLINGON FEMALE
B'ETOR DURAS

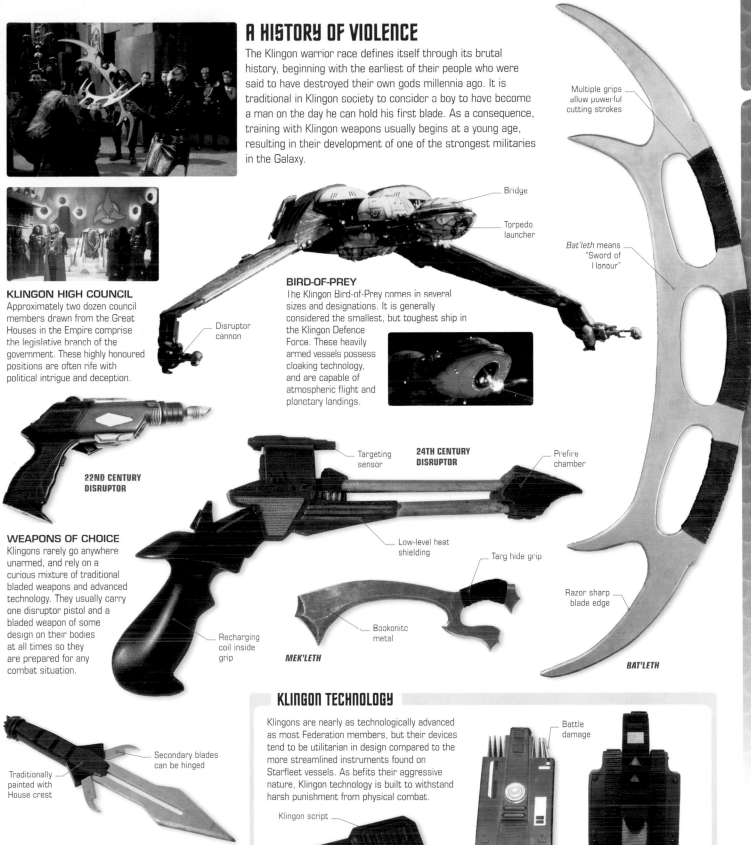

A HISTORY OF VIOLENCE

The Klingon warrior race defines itself through its brutal history, beginning with the earliest of their people who were said to have destroyed their own gods millennia ago. It is traditional in Klingon society to consider a boy to have become a man on the day he can hold his first blade. As a consequence, training with Klingon weapons usually begins at a young age, resulting in their development of one of the strongest militaries in the Galaxy.

Multiple grips allow powerful cutting strokes

Bat'leth means "Sword of Honour"

KLINGON HIGH COUNCIL

Approximately two dozen council members drawn from the Great Houses in the Empire comprise the legislative branch of the government. These highly honoured positions are often rife with political intrigue and deception.

BIRD-OF-PREY

The Klingon Bird-of-Prey comes in several sizes and designations. It is generally considered the smallest, but toughest ship in the Klingon Defence Force. These heavily armed vessels possess cloaking technology, and are capable of atmospheric flight and planetary landings.

Bridge

Torpedo launcher

Disruptor cannon

Targeting sensor

24TH CENTURY DISRUPTOR

Prefire chamber

22ND CENTURY DISRUPTOR

WEAPONS OF CHOICE

Klingons rarely go anywhere unarmed, and rely on a curious mixture of traditional bladed weapons and advanced technology. They usually carry one disruptor pistol and a bladed weapon of some design on their bodies at all times so they are prepared for any combat situation.

Low-level heat shielding

Targ hide grip

Baakonite metal

Recharging coil inside grip

MEK'LETH

Razor sharp blade edge

BAT'LETH

KLINGON TECHNOLOGY

Klingons are nearly as technologically advanced as most Federation members, but their devices tend to be utilitarian in design compared to the more streamlined instruments found on Starfleet vessels. As befits their aggressive nature, Klingon technology is built to withstand harsh punishment from physical combat.

Battle damage

Klingon script

Secondary blades can be hinged

Traditionally painted with House crest

D'K TAHG

The *d'k tahg* blade is a traditional Klingon weapon used for both hand-to-hand combat and ceremonial rites. It is often personalized with the owner's House crest painted on the handle and the theft of the blade is considered a serious insult to one's honour.

24TH CENTURY PADD   **23RD CENTURY COMMUNICATOR**   **TRICORDER**

KLINGON CULTURE

Clone of Kahless

KLINGON CULTURE is firmly rooted in the glorious past of the Klingon people, and the deeds of the mythical hero, Kahless. Its rituals are intended to celebrate or preserve an individual's honour while punishing those who exhibit disgraceful behaviour. Of particular note is the ritual in which a valiant death in battle is commemorated as a reward for a life well lived, and is used to announce the soul's arrival into the Klingon afterlife, *Sto-Vo-Kor*.

Claws of a dangerous predator

CONCERTINA

KAHLESS THE UNFORGETTABLE

Considered the greatest warrior to ever live, Kahless the Unforgettable is the foremost hero in Klingon mythology, and is credited with many great feats. His defeat of the evil tyrant, Morath, over a millennium earlier is celebrated as the birth of the Klingon Empire. Likewise, his romance with his love, Lady Lukara, and proposal following their battle against 500 enemy warriors is one of the greatest romantic tales of their people. It was foretold that he would one day return, which did indeed occur in the 24th century, albeit through the science of cloning.

BARGE OF THE DEAD
The Barge of the Dead ferries dishonoured souls to their final resting place in *Gre'thor*. Kortar, the first Klingon, captains the ship for all eternity as a punishment for slaying the gods millennia ago.

GRE'THOR
Gre'thor is the Klingon equivalent of the underworld, where dishonoured souls go after death. Klingons do not believe in a devil, but the mythical monster *Fek'lhr* is said to guard the gates of *Gre'thor*. Beyond those gates, the dead suffer an eternity of torture in the pit of despair as punishment for their dishonour.

THE BORETH MONASTERY
The planet Boreth is the most sacred place in the Empire, where it was believed Kahless would return. His followers established a monastery on the planet, and used DNA from the long-deceased figure to create a clone to lead them once again.

Ancient Klingon script

Distinctive central blade differs from typical *bat'leth*

Emblem of the Klingon Empire

THE SWORD OF KAHLESS

The first *bat'leth* (sword of honour) is said to have been forged by Kahless after dipping a lock of his hair into the fiery lava of the Kri'stak volcano and then cooling it in the Lake of Lursor, before bending it into the now famous shape of the blade. Following the death of Kahless the sword became a venerated symbol of the Klingon people, and was wrapped in a cover called the Shroud of the Sword. The Sword was later stolen by a species known as the Hur'q when they invaded Qo'noS, and has been lost for centuries.

KLINGON CEREMONIES

Klingons take their traditions very seriously. Rarely does a life event pass without some form of ceremony attached to it. Klingons honour themselves and their ancestry through rituals that often incorporate combat, bloodletting or pain in some form, with the ultimate celebration being over the honourable death of a comrade felled in combat. Klingons are so beholden to these traditions that they strictly adhere to them even when they conflict with their own best interests.

WORF AND JADZIA
The wedding between Worf, Son of Mogh, and Jadzia Dax on the Federation space station *Deep Space 9* is a blessed event, and an example of a traditional Klingon marriage ceremony. Sadly, their union is brief as Jadzia will be dead within the year, a tragic casualty of the Dominion War.

Red is often associated with Klingon ceremonies

BLOODWINE BARREL

Ingredients of bloodwine remain a mystery to non-Klingons

Targ tusk cork

Specially designed barrels keep bloodwine warm

KLINGON LANGUAGE
The guttural Klingon language consists of 80 dialects built around a flexible syntax. The written script utilizes lines of sharp, blade-like symbols.

Spiked glove for ritual combat

BLOODWINE
This red wine is consumed during most Klingon ceremonies, as well as on other occasions deemed worthy of celebration, such as victory in battle. It is considered to be at its best when served at a warm temperature. Other races find it to be a highly potent alcoholic beverage.

Used for wedding ceremonies

Bloodstones

WEDDING GOBLET
In addition to *bat'leths* and knives, there are many other, less lethal, trappings of Klingon ceremonies. These include targ tallow candles and goblets filled with bloodwine.

KLINGON WEDDING ATTIRE

Sacred sword stand

KLINGON FOOD

Klingon foods, like revenge, are dishes best served cold – or raw, to be specific – and still alive whenever possible. *Gagh*, or serpent worms, are the most well-known Klingon delicacy. Although they can be served stewed, eating *gagh* raw is preferred for the unique experience of the live food being digested.

KLINGON WEDDINGS

Klingon weddings follow a strict set of protocols, beginning days before the ceremony, when the groom and his attendants begin a ritual fast on the physical and spiritual journey known as the *kal'Hyah*. Meanwhile, the bride has her own series of arduous tasks to accomplish before the Lady of the groom's House will welcome her into the family. The ceremony itself includes the groom reciting the Klingon story of creation, followed by simulated battle between the couple and ending with ritual combat among the wedding party.

THE ROMULAN STAR EMPIRE

Brow ridge (differs from the smooth brow of the Vulcans)

ROMULAN MALE COMMANDER SURAN

Two thousand years ago, a group of Vulcans abandoned their homeworld to form their own society, rejecting the form of enlightenment promised by the teachings of the philosopher Surak. After centuries of searching for a new home, they settled on the planets Romulus and Remus to establish the Romulan Star Empire. Since then, the Romulans have fought wars with many of their neighbours in the universe, including Humanity in the 22nd century. They have made some moves toward reconciliation with the Federation in the 24th century, but remain a xenophobic and secretive race, quick to anger and reluctant to trust anyone.

ROMULUS

The primary homeworld of the Romulans and the location of their capital city has been described as a place of unparalleled beauty. Few Federation members have visited the planet, but those who have speak admirably of the firefalls of Gal Gath'thong, the Valley of Chula and the Apnex Sea.

24th century military uniform

ROMULAN EMBLEM

Those Vulcans who refused to follow Surak marched under the banner of the raptor. Consequently, the emblem of the Romulan Star Empire resembles a large avian creature, clutching two eggs symbolizing Romulus and Remus. The avian theme carries through the design of many Romulan starships.

ROMULAN SOCIETY

Government service is at the cornerstone of Romulan Society, whether in their ruling body of the Senate or their proud military. This dignified race holds their service members in reverence, and military or political rank are primary indicators of social status. At the same time it is a society riddled with fear and paranoia, especially of the brutal secret intelligence organization, the *Tal Shiar*. Romulans are xenophobic and distrustful of others, though they have entered into alliances with the Klingons and the Federation when it suited their purposes. Still, they remain a highly untrustworthy people, prone to treachery and violence in the course of achieving their goals.

ROMULANS IN THE 23RD CENTURY

A century after the Earth–Romulan War, tensions were still high among the two interstellar powers even though the Romulans had largely retreated to their territory to live as an isolationist society. That changed in the year 2266 when a Romulan ship ventured into Federation space for the first time in a century, and destroyed several Federation outposts.

Romulans of this period had a greater focus on political power grabs than their descendents, and their schemes tended to be plotted with cold calculation rather than the heated emotions associated with the Klingon race.

ROMULAN FEMALE
SENATOR TAL'AURA

Pointed ears show common ancestry with the Vulcans

24th century senatorial robe

ROMULAN DISRUPTORS

Romulans are one of several races in the Galaxy that arm themselves with disruptor weapons, a particularly nasty equivalent to the Federation's phasers. Disruptor technology works by breaking up the molecular bonds in a target, and can be integrated into handheld weapons as well as mounted on warships.

Trigger with Romulan script

Forward grip

Display

DISRUPTOR RIFLE

ROMULAN SCRIPT

The Romulan language is similar to Vulcan in many ways, most notably in the fact that it is read vertically from the left side of the page to the right. Although Romulan script features bulkier block lettering, the three spoken dialects of the Romulan people are almost indistinguishable to the Vulcan language for most outsiders.

THE ROMULAN SENATE

The government of the Romulan Star Empire is centred on the Senate, under the leadership of a Praetor. For the most part, the Romulan people hold members of the governing body in the highest esteem, but in the year 2379 a Reman coup leads to the assassination of all but one of the senators.

SPACECRAFT

The Romulans have an impressive armada of ships that come in a variety of designs, many of which follow the avian theme of the Romulan emblem. Romulan vessels incorporate advanced cloaking technology, and the Bird-of-Prey and Warbird designations in their fleet are some of the largest and most powerful vessels in the Alpha and Beta Quadrants, outgunning anything in Starfleet.

Two-person cockpit

Reman design

SCORPION ATTACK FIGHTER

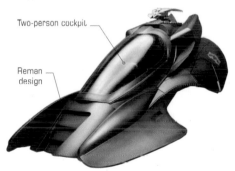

Armour plating in feathered design

Warp nacelles powered by forced quantum singularity

Unique "open shell" ship layout

Primary weapons systems

ROMULAN WARBIRD
D'DERIDEX-CLASS

ROMULAN INTRIGUE

BY THE MIDDLE of the 22nd century the Romulans were growing concerned about the Coalition of Planets that the Humans were working to form with their allies. Such an interstellar power would be a threat to the Empire, and they knew they had to undermine it. Several Romulan attempts at destabilizing the Coalition failed, and eventually open conflict erupted. The subsequent Earth–Romulan War, however, only strengthened the Coalition, leading to the formation of the Federation and centuries of mutual tensions, espionage and intrigue.

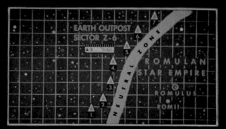

A HISTORY OF "CLOAK AND DAGGER"

The Romulans have a long history of deceptive practices, often working behind the scenes to develop tensions between neighbouring races, such as the Andorians and Tellarites. They take the view that if an enemy can be weakened from within, it will make destroying them from without all the easier. The secret intelligence agency within the Empire, the *Tal Shiar*, is an incredibly powerful organization, based in the capital and responsible for many of the encounters with the Federation over the centuries, while ruling with an iron fist over its own people.

23RD CENTURY ROMULAN WARBIRD

THE NEUTRAL ZONE
The peace treaty established at the end of the Earth–Romulan War identified an area of space that would serve as a buffer between the powers. Any incursion by either side into the Neutral Zone would be construed as an act of war.

Bends energy around a starship to render it completely invisible

CLOAKING DEVICE
The Romulan cloaking device is an advanced piece of technology that renders its ships completely invisible to sensors, giving them the tactical advantage of being able to approach a foe undetected, or escape without being followed.

Drone ship is a heavily-modified Romulan Warbird

Holographic emitters allow ship to take on appearance of other vessels

THE ENTERPRISE INCIDENT
The Romulans remain on their side of the Neutral Zone, unseen, for a hundred years, until briefly crossing into Federation space in 2266. Soon after, the *U.S.S. Enterprise* makes an incursion into the Zone under orders to steal a cloaking device from a female Romulan commander.

Sensor array

Tri-phasic disruptor emitters

Command rank insignia

Warbird command chair

COMMANDER TORETH

ROMULAN DRONE SHIP
This 22nd century experimental starship is a small but heavily armed attack vessel designed to be piloted remotely and covertly from the planet Romulus. As the ship is unmanned, most of the interior lacks life support systems, and it contains an advanced self-repair system to fix damage sustained on a mission.

THE MILITARY AND THE TAL SHIAR
Service in the military is considered one of the greatest achievements in Romulan society. Although the military is the face of the Empire, it is often in conflict with the secretive *Tal Shiar*. Commander Toreth, for example, is a decorated ship commander in the Romulan military, but deeply resents the *Tal Shiar* for murdering her father for speaking out against the government.

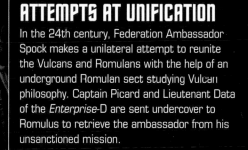

ATTEMPTS AT UNIFICATION

In the 24th century, Federation Ambassador Spock makes a unilateral attempt to reunite the Vulcans and Romulans with the help of an underground Romulan sect studying Vulcan philosophy. Captain Picard and Lieutenant Data of the *Enterprise*-D are sent undercover to Romulus to retrieve the ambassador from his unsanctioned mission.

ROMULAN BETRAYAL

Spock's invitation to Romulus is actually a Romulan trap in disguise, but the ambassador manages to thwart an invasion of Vulcan, and then remains on Romulus to continue his work.

THE PROMETHEUS

In another bold plot, the Romulans hijack the *U.S.S. Prometheus*, a 24th century prototype Starfleet vessel with an experimental multi-vector assault mode, that allows the ship to split into three separate craft for combat. A pair of Starfleet Emergency Medical Holograms (EMHs) that are left on board thwart the plan by overpowering the Romulan crew, and then use the *Prometheus* to destroy a Romulan ship that is giving chase.

THE REMANS

The Remans are a telepathic offshoot race enslaved by the Romulans. They inhabit the dark side of the planet Remus, which is locked in rotation with its orbit so that they never see the sun. As a result, they are incredibly sensitive to light. For centuries, the Remans were unable to break free of their Romulan oppressors who kept them enslaved, working in the dilithium mines on their homeworld. In the year 2379, they assassinate the Romulan Senate according to the plan of fellow slave, Shinzon – a clone of Captain Jean-Luc Picard.

THE COUP

Using a handheld thalaron radiation device, the Remans are able to eliminate the Senate with the help of a Romulan co-conspirator. The vicious weapon destroys all life within the Senate chamber. Shinzon then takes control of the Empire, proclaiming himself Praetor.

Disruptor rifle
with bayonet

Pale skin from
sunlight
deprivation

Double-shadow
blade design

Breaks open
to release
radiation

Reman
combat
uniform

REMAN DAGGER

REMAN WARRIORS

The Remans are powerful warriors, and prior to the coup the Romulans often used them as shock troops in warfare and as bodyguards for senators.

THE SCIMITAR

With Praetor Shinzon's sights now set on the Federation, his warship, *Scimitar*, is key to the attempted Reman coup. It is a huge vessel armed with an impressive array of weapons. Foremost among its armaments are thalaron radiation emitters capable of consuming organic matter on a scale large enough to destroy all life on Earth.

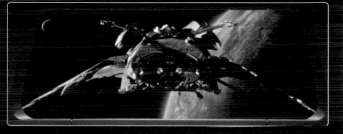

DEEP SPACE 9

POSITIONED BY THE ENTRANCE of a stable wormhole to the Gamma Quadrant, the *Deep Space 9* space station has, completely by chance, become the most strategically located Federation outpost in the 24th century. The station was annexed from the Cardassians when they abandoned their claim to the planet Bajor, which had been under their oppressive regime for years, leaving this former mining station behind. The Bajoran Provisional Government has invited Starfleet to operate the station jointly while they consider membership in the Federation.

THE PROMENADE
One of the more important facets of the space station is the large commercial space known as the Promenade. This boasts a diverse range of attractions from a holy Bajoran Temple to the somewhat more sordid Quark's Bar.

BAJORAN WORMHOLE
The Bajoran Wormhole is a stable passageway in space that can transport vessels from the Alpha Quadrant to a location in the Gamma Quadrant over 70,000 light years away. This incredibly rare phenomenon has opened up deep space travel, introducing both exciting new worlds and dangerous threats.

U.S.S. DEFIANT NX-74205

The *U.S.S. Defiant* is a prototype Starfleet vessel stationed at *Deep Space 9*, and named after another Federation ship from a century earlier. This version of the *Defiant* was specifically built as a heavily armed escort vessel to counter the Borg threat to the Federation. It is later pressed into service during the Dominion War, under the command of Benjamin Sisko. It is notably the sole Federation vehicle in possession of a Romulan cloaking device, on loan for the war. The original prototype is destroyed in battle in 2375, but replaced by the *U.S.S. Sao Paulo* (renamed the *Defiant II*) soon after.

Sensor pallet

Multimission module pack

Hull made from duranium composites

Crew cockpit seats four

DANUBE-CLASS RUNABOUT

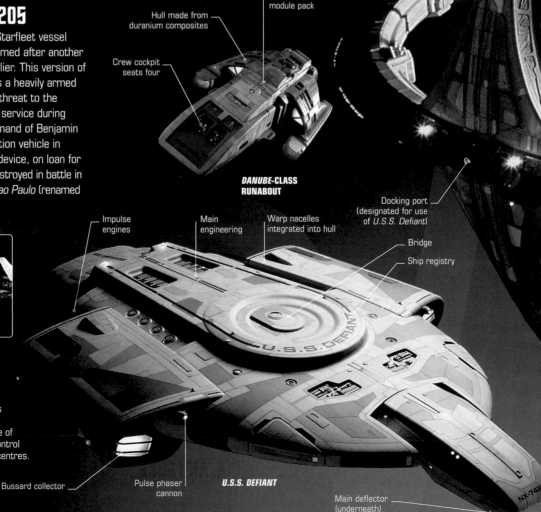

Docking port (designated for use of *U.S.S. Defiant*)

Bridge

Ship registry

Impulse engines

Main engineering

Warp nacelles integrated into hull

U.S.S. DEFIANT BRIDGE
Like the ship itself, the bridge of the *Defiant* is smaller than that of most 24th century Federation starships, but it is a battle-ready tactical and navigational centre. The flight control and operations station in front of the command chair combines two systems into one for ease of use, while stations around the bridge control science systems, sensors and tactical centres.

Bussard collector

Pulse phaser cannon

U.S.S. DEFIANT

Main deflector (underneath)

NX-74205

■ **STATION OVERVIEW** ■

- OVERALL DIAMETER: 1,451 metres (4,760 feet)
- RESIDENTS: 300–2,000 (maximum capacity 7,000)
- CONSTRUCTION COMPLETED: 2351

TEROK NOR

Deep Space 9 was originally the Cardassian mining station *Terok Nor,* prior to being taken over by the Bajorans and Federation. During the Cardassian occupation of Bajor, slave labour was used to construct the station, with prisoners then forced to process raw uridium ore while living in community quarters that were effectively labour camps. When the wormhole was first discovered near Bajor, *Deep Space 9* was moved out of Bajoran orbit and placed adjacent to this important new phenomenon.

Upper docking pylon

Deflector assembly

Runabout landing pad

Operations module

Promenade

Habitat ring

Defense sail contains weapon mounts and tractor beam emitters

Major cross member

Station core

Fusion generator

Sensor pallet

Docking ring

Lower docking pylon

CARDASSIAN CONSTRUCTION
Built to Cardassian specifications, *Deep Space 9* differs from any other Starfleet posting. Control consoles are covered with Cardassian script, and the often-failing Cardassian technical systems on the station provide unique challenges to the Starfleet engineering crew assigned to it.

OPERATIONS CENTER
Located in the topmost section of the station's upper core, the Operations Centre, or Ops, is the command centre of the station. From Ops, the Starfleet and Bajoran command crew can track all station functions, sensors, and tactical systems.

CAPTAIN SISKO

WHEN COMMANDER Benjamin Sisko is posted to *Deep Space 9* he is on the verge of resigning his commission, until his new role assisting the Bajorans with their admittance into the Federation turns into something rather more complex. The discovery of the Bajoran Wormhole, Sisko's naming as Bajor's Emissary to the Prophets, and the coming Dominion War show him to be a courageous and selfless leader, winning him a more prominent role in Starfleet and a promotion to captain.

24th century Command uniform (*c.* 2373 design update)

Retractable sight with heads-up display

Power cell

TYPE-3 PHASER
An updated variant of the type-3 phaser rifle is introduced in the 2360s. It features 16 beam settings, and becomes the standard field weapon for Federation ground forces during the Dominion War.

ON THE FRONT LINES

When Dominion forces in the Gamma Quadrant declare war on the Federation, *Deep Space 9*'s location at the mouth of the Bajoran Wormhole immediately puts Captain Sisko on the front lines of the confrontation. Odo, his Chief of Security – one of the few members of the enemy race on the Federation's side – also gives Sisko unique insight into the conflict. Sisko plays an important role in the war effort, providing strategic and tactical information to Starfleet. He facilitates the commissioning of the *U.S.S. Defiant*, liaises with the Klingons, uncovers a coup attempt on Earth and is surreptitiously responsible for the Romulans' entry into the war on the side of the Federation.

Command division stripe

A favourite beverage of Captain Sisko

STARFLEET COMMUNICATOR
The Starfleet combadge undergoes a subtle design change in the early 2370s, becoming sleeker.

SAURIAN BRANDY

JENNIFER SISKO

Captain Sisko's first wife, Jennifer, was killed fighting the Borg at the Battle of Wolf 359. Sisko mourns her loss for years, partially blaming her death on Jean-Luc Picard who led the Borg attack while under their control. The Bajoran Prophets help Sisko move on through a brief vision of the pair together again.

PERSONAL RELATIONSHIPS

Like many Starfleet officers, Benjamin Sisko sometimes finds balancing duty with his personal life to be a challenge. He blames himself and his posting on the *U.S.S. Saratoga* for his first wife's death and has to move past that guilt before he can fully commit to someone new, in the form of Kasidy Yates. He also realizes the importance of the time he spends with his son from his first marriage, Jake. Tragically, his role as the Emissary to the Bajoran Prophets ultimately takes him away from his loved ones to assume a higher calling.

KASIDY YATES

Sisko finds love again with Kasidy Yates, a civilian freighter captain who takes work in the Bajoran sector to keep herself close to *Deep Space 9*. The couple eventually marry and Kasidy becomes pregnant with a child that Sisko will sadly never meet.

San Francisco Giants baseball team cap

JAKE SISKO

Raising a son alone while commanding a space station is not easy, but Jake Sisko is not just Benjamin's son, he is a best friend as well.

BASEBALL AND MITT

Antique baseball is one of Sisko's most prized possessions

BASEBALL

One of Sisko's personal interests is baseball, a sport that orginated on Earth, but died out in the mid-21st century. Sisko enjoys watching holographic recreations of famous players, and even creates a *Deep Space 9* team – the "Niners."

Handmade by Sisko while he was under the influence of the alien Saltah'na race.

Telescope

SALTAH'NA CLOCK

SISKO'S CREOLE KITCHEN

Joseph Sisko, Benjamin's father, is the owner and chef behind this Earth restaurant in the French Quarter of New Orleans. Following the death of his friend, Jadzia Dax, Benjamin leaves *Deep Space 9* and spends several months working at the restaurant, playing piano there and mourning the losses of the Dominion War.

Used by Sisko to pilot his replica Bajoran lightship

EMISSARY OF THE PROPHETS

Ancient Bajoran prophecies tell of an Emissary who will one day unite their people and find the Celestial Temple that is home to their gods, the Prophets. When Sisko arrives at *Deep Space 9* he discovers the Bajoran Wormhole, which is home to a race of aliens that claim to be those Prophets. As a result the Bajorans name him their Emissary, though Sisko is initially reluctant to claim the religious title. Eventually he comes to accept his role, and embraces Bajoran culture, even building a replica of an ancient Bajoran vessel known as a lightship. Ultimately Sisko sacrifices himself to save their world, which gains him admittance into the Celestial Temple.

THE RELUCTANT EMISSARY

To begin with, Sisko is uncomfortable with his position as a spiritual leader to the Bajoran people. But that does not stop him from fulfilling his part in prophecy, even when it means potentially unleashing devastating powers.

BAJORAN SEXTANT

Dual arc scale

CAPT. SISKO'S CREW

THE INITIAL COMMAND CREW of *Deep Space 9* consists of a team of Starfleet officers and Bajoran representatives, working together as the Bajoran government prepares for admission into the Federation. Their varied approaches to life cause problems at first as the crew work to integrate their different personalities, but their commitment to their mission brings them together as comrades and friends.

Chief warrant officer rank pip

PADD (personal access display device)

KIRA NERYS

The highest-ranking Bajoran representative on the station, Kira is a former resistance fighter who rebelled against the Cardassian occupation. Living under harsh Cardassian rule for most of her life hardened Kira, making her suspicious of alien governments, including the Federation. As a deeply religious person she has a difficult time reconciling the fact that her superior officer is also a religious icon, but she eventually softens to Sisko and the rest of the Federation crew.

Used when replicators are unavailable

STARFLEET EMERGENCY RATIONS

MILES O'BRIEN

Miles O'Brien became chief of operations on *Deep Space 9* following a promotion and transfer from the *Enterprise*-D. This beloved husband and father is a career Starfleet officer with over 30 years of engineering experience. His technical know-how is handy in a station that had been abandoned in a state of ill-repair, though he often encounters challenges integrating his Federation training with the station's Cardassian systems.

24th century Bajoran militia command uniform

Changeling taking humanoid form

Bajoran militia security officer uniform

FEDERATION ISOLINEAR CHIPS

Utilized for data storage

ODO

Odo is *Deep Space 9*'s chief of security. His name comes from the Cardassian word for "nothing", *Odo'ital*. Found as an orphaned infant, this member of a changeling race can assume any form, but had no idea who he was or the people he had come from. Odo was raised in a laboratory on Bajor, before rising to the rank of security chief of *Terok Nor*, and was able to stay on in his role when the Federation took control of the station. After years of searching, Odo discovers that he comes from a Gamma Quadrant race known as the Founders, who lead the Dominion.

ODO'S BUCKET
Every 16 hours, Odo's body must revert to its natural liquid state. As such, he does not have a bed in his quarters, only a bucket in which he rests.

DR JULIAN BASHIR

At the age of six, Julian Bashir's parents had their son undergo an illegal genetic resequencing procedure to correct a severe learning disability. Bashir's artificially enhanced intellect allowed him to pursue his interest in medicine while his advanced physical prowess was used to great effect on the racquetball team at Starfleet Medical Academy. As an adult, the doctor indulges in his adventurous side by requesting a post on the frontier at *Deep Space 9*, where he becomes the chief medical officer, working to relieve the suffering of others.

Shoulder strap

Personalized carrying case

DR. JULIAN BASHIR, M.D., FASFS

RACQUETBALL
Julian Bashir was captain of the Starfleet Medical Academy racquetball team, playing a modern version of a game created on Earth centuries earlier.

Racquet design has evolved since the 20th century

Medical tricorder

Genetically enhanced strength and stamina

Emitter regulates regenerative beam

DERMAL REGENERATOR
This piece of equipment is used to rapidly repair minor skin wounds, cuts and burns. It can also be used to remove scars.

Controls adjustable by injury type and severity

QUARK

Although not a member of the crew, this Ferengi bartender and businessman runs the local watering hole on *Deep Space 9*, while being up to his ears in a number of nefarious deals that keeps him at odds with the chief of security, Odo.

Liquor bottles

Trill spots

EZRI DAX
Less than a year into her marriage, Jadzia Dax becomes a casualty of war. Medical complications ensue while the surviving Dax symbiont is en route to Trill. The only course of action is to join the symbiont with the lone Trill onboard, an assistant counsellor named Ezri who has never been prepared for joining.

Joining with the Dax symbiont causes Ezri to change from being right-handed to left-handed

Promoted to lieutenant commander

Baldric with symbol of House of Mogh

WORF AND JADZIA DAX

Deep Space 9's Trill science officer, Jadzia Dax, rekindles an old friendship when she comes to the station, as the previous host to the Dax symbiont, Curzon, had been close friends with Commander Sisko. But new friendships are also formed when Lieutenant Commander Worf transfers from the *Enterprise*-D a few years later to serve as strategic operations officer. On the surface, Jadzia's mischievous, devil-may-care attitude and Worf's stoic dignity would seem to be at odds with one another, but these opposites develop an attraction that makes them an interesting pair.

THE BAJORANS

THE BAJORANS ARE AN ANCIENT RACE with a culture dating back over half a million years. For most of their history they were a peaceful and deeply spiritual people until the Cardassian occupation of their world forced many to become resistance fighters. When the Cardassians were finally driven off the planet, the Bajoran Provisional Government requested assistance from the United Federation of Planets, allowing the Federation to exercise joint control of the now-abandoned Cardassian space station *Terok Nor* – renamed *Deep Space 9* – in return.

BAJOR
Bajor is one of two inhabitable worlds in a system of 14 planets. Orbited by several moons, Bajor is rich in natural resources, which is a large part of the reason it was a tempting target for the Cardassians.

Nasal ridges

Earring traditionally worn on right ear

Faith symbol communicator

Rank pin

Tracer beam focuses primary energy discharge

BAJORAN WEAPONS
Bajoran weapons made great advancements during the time of the Cardassian occupation, in spite of the fact that their development and manufacture by the resistance had to be kept secret. The Bajoran militia is now armed with both phaser pistols and rifles.

Trigger

Makes distinctive sound when fired

BAJORAN PHASER PISTOL

Firing settings

Trigger

BAJORAN PHASER RIFLE

Bajoran faith symbol features on weapons

BAJORAN SOCIETY

Bajoran society is in the process of rebuilding following decades of brutal oppression under Cardassian rule. This deeply religious people place a great deal of faith in their religious leaders and the Prophets they follow. Prior to the occupation, Bajorans lived under the strict caste system of *D'jarras* in which a family's status in society was set and would determine the very jobs the family members could hold. The Bajorans abolished this caste system when they were forced to work together as a people to fight against their Cardassian oppressors.

TECHNOLOGY
Bajorans may have been travelling the stars for centuries longer than Humans, but the stagnation of Cardassian rule means that their technology is now slightly inferior to that of the Federation.

Display screen

BAJORAN FEMALE KIRA NERYS

Bajoran fondness for gold colours extends to their technology

Control keys

Bajoran militia uniform

BAJORAN TRICORDER

Handheld computer library access

BAJORAN PADD

BAJORAN RELIGION

Bajorans worship a group of spiritual entities known as the Prophets, who they believe reside in a place called the Celestial Temple. The Prophets are credited with creating nine Orbs known as "The Tears of the Prophets" to provide wisdom and guidance to the people of Bajor. Long ago, a group of malevolent beings known as Pah-wraiths were banished from the Celestial Temple by the Prophets, and confined to the fire caves of Bajor. The struggle between the Prophets and Pah-wraiths has supposedly continued for millennia, and plays a major part in Bajoran religious tradition. It was long prophesied that an Emissary of the Prophets would reveal the location of the Celestial Temple and unite the Bajorans. Commander Benjamin Sisko of Starfleet reluctantly fulfils that destiny and is declared to be the Emissary.

THE KAI

The supreme religious leader of Bajor is an elected position that is as much a political role as it is a spiritual one. The *Kai* exercises a great deal of influence over the Bajoran people, which is a tempting power when in the wrong hands.

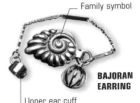

- Family symbol
- Upper ear cuff

BAJORAN EARRING

LANGUAGE

Bajoran script is comprised of symbols that can be read differently depending on the rotation in which each icon is displayed.

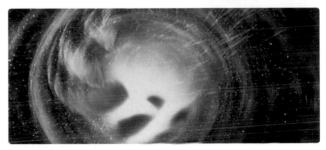

THE CELESTIAL TEMPLE

The Celestial Temple is the name given by the Bajorans to the wormhole in their sector, following its discovery by Benjamin Sisko. Many Bajorans believe that the extra-dimensional aliens living inside are their gods, the Prophets.

BAJORAN ORB

- Orb case
- Exposure to orb can produce brief, intense visions
- Bajoran gemstone
- Doors open to reveal the orb inside

RUINS OF B'HALA

The ancient city of B'hala has been lost to the Bajorans for over 20,000 years, until the Emissary experiences a vision providing the location of the ruins. Beneath the ruins of the holy city an even older site is found with a stone tablet prophesying an epic battle called "The Reckoning". Sisko's destruction of the tablet unleashes the spirits of a Prophet and a Pah-wraith who then clash on board *Deep Space 9*, in the possessed bodies of Kira Nerys and Sisko's son.

BAJORAN SPRING WINE

- Faith symbol
- Used in Bajoran wedding ceremonies
- Made from fermented kava juice

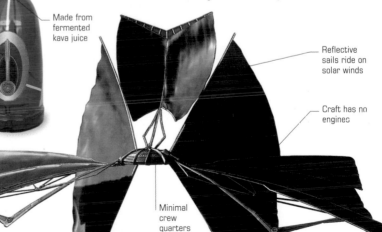

- Reflective sails ride on solar winds
- Craft has no engines
- Minimal crew quarters

BAJORAN EXPLORERS

Bajorans first experienced space travel during Earth's 16th century, on solar sail vessels powered by light pressure from Bajor's sun. The Cardassians believed this pre-warp form of travel a myth until Benjamin Sisko created a functioning ship from a set of ancient plans.

BAJORAN LIGHTSHIP

- Played to gather Bajorans to temple

BAJORAN HARP

THE CARDASSIAN UNION

THE CARDASSIANS DISPLAY a complex mixture of the Klingon warrior spirit with the Romulan penchant for intrigue and subterfuge. The lack of resources on Cardassia Prime forced this once highly cultural people to build their military into a powerful force that takes what they need to survive. This has resulted in repeated conflicts with the other powers of the Alpha and Beta Quadrants. Even the peace treaty signed with the Federation in 2367 at the end of the Border Wars is nullified only a few years later by the Cardassians' entry into the Dominion War.

CARDASSIA PRIME
What the Cardassian homeworld lacks in natural resources, it makes up for with prized archeological treasures from its more civilized past. Tragically, many of these artefacts are plundered and sold off to fund the Cardassian war machine.

CARDASSIAN SOCIETY

The Cardassian Union is led by the Central Command, a militaristic government that is respected and feared. It applies harsh punishments to those who engage in illegal acts, under laws that designate guilt before a trial is held. Officially power rests in a civilian administration called the *Detapa* council, but its powers are limited. Families are central to Cardassian society with the elderly being revered. However, this does not extend to children resulting from unions between Cardassians and Bajorans that occurred during the occupation of the planet Bajor, who are traditionally shunned by society.

INTERACTION WITH STARFLEET
Feelings of bitterness flow through both sides in the wars between the Federation and Cardassians. The Cardassians have been guilty of numerous inhumane acts, and even Starfleet officers have been known to bend the rules to see justice done.

Teardrop impression, also appears on centre of chest

Baseball from Earth

Neck ridge

CARDASSIAN MALE
GUL DUKAT

24th century military uniform

Bajoran nasal ridges

Cardassian facial ridges

Blended skin colouring

CARDASSIAN / BAJORAN HYBRID
TORA ZIYAL

Cardassian female clothing

THE CARDASSIAN MILITARY

The Cardassian military and its powerful fleet, formerly under the leadership of the Central Command, is a major force in the Alpha and Beta Quadrants. Their rank structure parallels that of Starfleet, with a *Legate* as a ranking member of the Central Command, a *Gul* being the commanding officer of a vessel, and a *Glinn* its first officer. In the latter part of the 24th century, a dissident movement among the populace takes control of the military, returning power to the people and shifting rule from the Central Command to the *Detapa* Council.

Warp engines

Command section

Main targeting system

Forward weapons array

GALOR-CLASS ATTACK CRUISER

Beam intensity and width adjustment

Isotolinium power cell

Emitter crystal

PHASE-DISRUPTOR RIFLE

The Cardassian phase-disruptor pistol and phase-disruptor rifle are standard issue arms for the military. They are noted for their durability, and relatively simple components.

Display screen with Cardassian script

Control buttons rather than touch-screen interface

PADD

SPACE STATIONS

As part of the armistice agreement with the Federation at the end of the Border Wars, the Cardassians were forced to abandon their space stations in sectors no longer in their territory. Some of these stations, like *Empok Nor*, would lie dormant while others, such as *Terok Nor*, were handed over to the Bajorans and the Federation and remain in use.

Wall-mounted

REPLICATOR

Like Federation replicators, the Cardassian version is capable of rematerializing matter in different forms through the use of transporter technology. Replicators are primarily used for creating food, and units are placed throughout ships and space stations.

Control panel

Phase transition chamber

Toranium boronate casing

Display screen

CARDASSIAN CULTURE

Cardassians may be a militaristic race, but they have not completely forgotten their artistic heritage and culture. Cardassian drinks are enjoyed throughout the Galaxy, and the Cardassian Institute of the Arts presides over the modern art culture of their people, as their artists still play an important role in society.

Alcoholic beverage

TRICORDER

The Cardassian tricorder has limited functionality compared to the Federation design. The device tends to be used more as an emergency scanner, often reserved for the field of battle.

Powered by rechargeable isotolinium ampule

Sign with Cardassian script

LANGUAGE

The Cardassian language is written in thin rectangular blocks, which are arranged in vertical and horizontal sequences.

Has a viscous consistency

KANAR BOTTLE

CARDASSIAN TECHNOLOGY

Although the Cardassians are a warp-capable people their technology is not as advanced as that of the combined races of the Federation. Cardassian ships, for example, may be heavily armed but their shields are generally of inferior quality. When a joint Federation and Bajoran team assumes control of the space station formerly known as *Terok Nor*, Starfleet engineers have a difficult time adjusting to the comparatively unsophisticated alien technology. In fact they are forced to slip onto another abandoned Cardassian space station simply to obtain replacement parts.

CARDASSIAN TREACHERY

THE CARDASSIANS DO NOT have many allies. Their aggressive tendencies and combative nature have made them enemies of the Federation, Klingons, Romulans and most other power players in the Galaxy. Bajorans especially harbour deep-seated resentment towards their former oppressors. But it is the treacherous nature of the Cardassians themselves that has proven most destructive. The Union has been torn apart from the inside, and then attacked by enemies and former allies alike.

CARDASSIAN EMBLEM
The Symbol of the Cardassian Union resembles the shape of the *Galor*-class attack cruiser, stressing the importance of the military in their society.

THE BATTLE OF CARDASSIA
Cardassia Prime is left in ruins at the end of the Dominion War after the Cardassians turn on their Dominion allies to support the Federation. Enraged by the betrayal, the Dominion unleashes the full force of its fleet on the planet in a massacre that kills over 800 million people.

DIVIDED LOYALTIES

It is the Cardassian inclination for putting their own interests before all else that leads to their ultimate downfall. They first partner with the Dominion to have them deal with the Maquis rebellion. When the Breen enter the war, the Cardassians feel their influence slipping and realize it is now in their best interest to side with the Federation. Changing sides will cost them dearly.

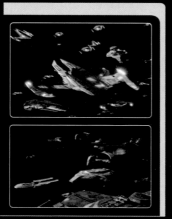

Uniform incorporates chest armour

Scales

GUL DUKAT

Dukat was the final prefect to oversee Bajor before the emancipation of the planet at the end of the Cardassian–Federation Border Wars. Dukat's star in the Union rises and falls in the following years, until secret negotiations to align his people with the Dominion lead him to become head of the Cardassian government. He continues to maintain ties with *Deep Space 9*, the space station that was once under his command, in the years after the armistice, and with Dominion help he retakes the station at the beginning of the Dominion War. His new role in the government is short-lived as he falls from grace and ultimately dies after coming under the influence of an extra-dimensional being called a Pah-wraith.

Wrist communicator

Damar

Cardassian script

Weyoun, Dominion ambassador to Cardassia

THE MAQUIS

The treaty between the Cardassians and the Federation that goes into effect in 2370 redefines the border between the two powers, forcing Federation colonists now on the wrong side of the lines to abandon their homes. The Maquis – an upstart group of colonists and Federation members sensitive to their plight – take up arms against the Cardassians to defend those homes. They quickly grow into a powerful force until a new partnership between the Dominion and Cardassians wipes the rebel group out.

THE MAQUIS EMBLEM

Maquis raider under attack

DAMAR

Dukat's first officer, Damar, lives by the questionable morals of his people only to have them turn on him like they turn against Cardassia itself. When Damar overhears Dukat's daughter confessing her role in a prisoner escape during the Dominion War, he kills her for the crime. He then usurps Dukat's position as liaison to the Dominion, opposite the Vorta ambassador, Weyoun. Turning to drink when he realizes that the Cardassians have lost their usefulness to the Dominion, he then betrays his former allies, and dies in battle on Cardassia.

PADD SHOWING CARDASSIAN–FEDERATION BORDER

Control buttons

Measuring units

Clothing designed by Garak himself

Cardassian phase-disruptor pistol

A SIMPLE TAILOR?
Cardassians have a reputation for being a deceptive race, hiding the truth for their benefit and protection. *Deep Space 9* resident Elim Garak claims to be an unremarkable tailor, yet his background hides much more…

Magnifying glass

TAILOR'S EYEPIECE

CARDASSIAN MANACLES

GARAK AND THE OBSIDIAN ORDER

Elim Garak's former membership in the Cardassian intelligence agency, the Obsidian Order, is one of the worst kept secrets on *Deep Space 9*. Garak knows that personal loyalty does not matter to the Order – Garak's own father, who leads the organization, exiled his son to *Deep Space 9* following the Cardassian withdrawal of Bajor. The Obsidian Order is supposedly under the direction of the *Detapa* Council, but in reality they have little oversight, often acting in an entirely independent fashion. In a joint mission with the Romulan secret police, the *Tal Shiar*, the Order launches a disastrous preemptive attack against the Dominion that effectively destroys the Order as an independent power.

PRISONERS OF WAR
The Cardassians' harsh treatment of their prisoners, such as those in forced labour camps in places like *Terok Nor*, is part of the reason they have engendered so much animosity across the Galaxy.

THE DOMINION

THE GAMMA QUADRANT has its own planetary alliance in the form of The Dominion, but it bears little resemblance to the United Federation of Planets. The Dominion consists of hundreds of worlds under the rule of the Founders, a powerful, but rarely seen race. The Vorta run the Founders' empire and the Jem'Hadar serve as their military might. A Dominion attack on the Alpha Quadrant causes massive destruction, but only succeeds in weakening the Dominion.

SYMBOL OF THE DOMINION

THE VORTA

The Vorta have been genetically engineered to serve the reclusive Founders as the face of the Dominion. They are a combination of diplomats and commanders, carrying out the Founders' wishes and maintaining control of the Jem'Hadar. As part of their engineering, the Vorta have been genetically coded to worship the Founders as gods. They have also been granted a kind of immortality in that they reproduce through cloning, making it possible for a Vorta to exist beyond death in a similar mind and body. Their gifts also come with limitations as the Founders only grant each individual Vorta the genetic traits needed to fill his or her role in society, as a means of keeping them from growing beyond their intended purpose.

Virtual display headset

Pale skin

WEYOUN
Multiple clones of Weyoun serve as the Dominion's chief liaison to the Cardassian Union during the Dominion War. It is a dangerous job and several of these clones die violently.

THE GREAT LINK
On their home planet the Founders merge in their liquid form, bonding their people in a unified experience of mind and body. This union, called the Great Link, is poisoned during the Dominion War, until Odo, a changeling who fights on the side of the Federation, returns to heal his people at the war's end.

The Vorta were genetically engineered from ape-like creatures

VORTA FEMALE KILANA

Can take on humanoid form

FOUNDER FEMALE

Morphogenic enzymes allow for shape-shifting abilities

THE FOUNDERS

The Founders are an ancient race of changelings that can assume any form, including the appearance of other aliens. Until the Dominion War, they existed almost exclusively in self-exile away from the "Solids" of the universe – their name for aliens that cannot change their form – who once hunted them out of fear. Still curious about the universe, the Founders sent 100 infants out to explore and return home with what they learned. Constable Odo of *Deep Space 9* is one of those infants, who grew up unaware of the importance of his people to the races of the Gamma Quadrant.

The Founders select one of their number to represent them during the Dominion War

THE DOMINION WAR

The Federation's exploration of the Gamma Quadrant after the opening of the Bajoran Wormhole causes concern among the Founders. Hoping to extend their reach into the Alpha Quadrant, the Founders infiltrate key positions in the Federation in disguise, working to destabilize the government from within. An alliance with the Cardassians turns them into a more significant threat and war is officially declared in 2373 with an attack on *Deep Space 9*. The war ravages the Cardassian homeworld, greatly weakens the Klingon Empire, and nearly causes the Founders' extinction while costing hundreds of millions of lives on both sides.

BRUTAL BATTLES

The Dominion War is fought on multiple fronts with the Dominion's nearly inexhaustible supply of genetically engineered Jem'Hadar soldiers inflicting considerable damage on Federation forces.

Footage of Jem'Hadar forces training prior to the siege of AR-558

Bridge

Vessel is over 1,200 meters (3,940 feet) in length

Thick reptilian skin

Boney protrusions

MILITARY FLEET

The Dominion fleet is a massive armada of vessels numbering in the thousands. Captain Benjamin Sisko has to call on the power of the Bajoran Prophets to protect *Deep Space 9* and, ultimately, all of the Alpha and Beta Quadrants when faced with this overwhelming force attempting to enter the Alpha Quadrant via the Bajoran Wormhole.

DOMINION BATTLESHIP

Warp nacelle

Locked cover

KETRACEL-WHITE STORAGE ARK

Supplies of ketracel-white are kept in locked containers, with access controlled by Vorta commanders to ensure loyalty among their Jem'Hadar troops. Ketracel-white withdrawal causes Jem'Hadar to lapse into violent insanity, followed by death.

Contains over a dozen vials of ketracel-white

Dagger

THE JEM'HADAR

When the Founders infiltrate the governments of the Alpha and Beta Quadrants, they do so by arriving incognito, replacing existing officials with changelings. But when they want to make overt moves against the Federation they send in their soldiers, the Jem'Hadar. These genetically-engineered warriors are the first line of Dominion offence, created to fight with inexhaustible bodies that require only the drug ketracel-white to function. They are specially bred to stand out as a threat and designed to look the part. What they lack in finesse is made up for with brute strength and resiliency.

JEM'HADAR SOLDIER

THE JEM'HADAR

THE JEM'HADAR HAVE BEEN GENETICALLY ENGINEERED to serve as soldiers for the Dominion military. Their entire existence is defined by their role in fighting for their leaders, the race known as the Founders. They are bred in birthing chambers where they mature at an accelerated rate and are designed to be dependent on a drug that both gives them nutrition and makes them pliable to command. They do not eat or sleep as they exist only to fight. As a result of their violent lifestyle, few Jem'Hadar live beyond 15 years of age.

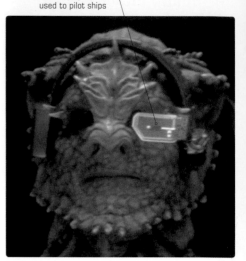

Visual display device used to pilot ships

JEM'HADAR PILOTS
The Jem'Hadar are particularly adept at physical combat, but they are also well trained in space warfare, piloting an armada of battle cruisers and smaller attack ships. A Jem'Hadar fleet, including over 150 vessels, easily overwhelms a smaller attack force of combined Romulan and Cardassian ships that attack the Founders' homeworld in 2371.

WARRIORS OF THE DOMINION

For the Jem'Hadar, combat is not merely a passion – it is their purpose in life. They are the soldiers of the Dominion taking orders from Vorta overseers, who in turn are in the service of the Founders. Most Jem'Hadar have never interacted directly with the Founders, and have elevated these rulers to the level of gods. This is in spite of the fact that their leaders keep the Jem'Hadar chemically drug-addicted to maintain control. Jem'Hadar have been known to take their own lives if they fail to protect a Founder and only consider themselves to be truly alive when in battle, supporting their belief that "Victory is life".

Hard outer dermal layer

Boney protrusions on head and body

Rear sight

Trigger

Superior vision

Enhanced olfactory senses

Stock

Ketracel-white tube

PHASED POLARON BEAM RIFLE
SOLDIER'S PRIMARY WEAPON

Ketracel-white tube

KETRACEL-WHITE

"White", as it is simply known among the Jem'Hadar, is a drug the Founders have genetically engineered their soldier's bodies to be addicted to. This isogenic enzyme is necessary for their survival, and is carefully administered from vials into tubes surgically implanted in their necks.

Storage vial

Cap (closed position)

BRED FOR BATTLE

Jem'Hadar soldiers are engineered in artificial birthing chambers, and this lack of a need for sexual reproduction is the reason there are no Jem'Hadar females. Jem'Hadar become fully mature within three days of leaving their birthing chambers, by which time they are already physically stronger than a Human and are prepared to begin their training. Their skin becomes increasingly reptilian as they age, and a Jem'Hadar who reaches 20 is referred to as an "Honoured Elder."

Kar'takin

JEM'HADAR WEAPONS

The weapons of the Jem'Hadar are particularly vicious instruments, made even more lethal in the capable hands of this warrior race. Like Klingons, the Jem'Hadar focus on bladed weapons for hand-to-hand combat. Their firearms come with a unique feature that adds chemical enhancements like nerve agents and anti-coagulants to the particle stream, which can disable or kill a wounded target.

Camouflage ability renders body invisible to scanners and the naked eye

Ketracel-white tube

Stabbing point

KAR'TAKIN

Two-handed strokes enable weapon to slice through enemies with ease

Front sight

Particle stream enhancement controls

Pulsed polaron beam generator

Emitter is made from solid arkenium

Non-configurable energy settings

Emitter

Grip

Resilient body can shrug off hits from phasers set to stun

Uniform designed to protect the wearer from anti-personnel force fields

Dual-bladed combat knife

Pole arms are favoured by Jem'Hadar

TRAINING WEAPON

Characteristic dual-bladed design

PHASED POLARON BEAM PISTOL
SOLDIER'S SECONDARY WEAPON

JEM'HADAR SOLDIER

U.S.S. VOYAGER NCC-74656

IN 2371 THE FEDERATION CREW of the Starship *Voyager* is dispatched on a mission into the Badlands—an area of space teeming with plasma storms—to capture a renegade Maquis ship. During the operation a powerful alien entity pulls the ship 70,000 light years across space into the Delta Quadrant. Under the command of Captain Kathryn Janeway, leading a combined Starfleet and Maquis crew, *Voyager* is forced to make the long journey back to the Alpha Quadrant through unexplored space, totally alone.

ENGINEERING
With *Voyager* stranded thousands of light years away from the nearest Starfleet repair station or spare parts, its engineering department requires firm but gentle hands to keep it running. At times, this requires some unsanctioned improvisation, including the addition of Borg technology.

Aft upper sensor array

Shuttle bay

Impulse engine

Warp nacelle

Variable geometry nacelle pylon

SICKBAY
Voyager's sickbay is equipped with an Emergency Medical Hologram, originally intended as a temporary replacement for the ship's doctor. Holoprojectors around the room create a hologram that adopts a Human form, to serve the medical needs of the crew on a short-term basis. *Voyager*'s EMH is pressed into long-term service as all of the ship's medical staff are killed when the ship is pulled into the Delta Quadrant.

THE INTREPID-CLASS

Voyager is an *Intrepid*-class starship. This is one of the smaller ship designs in the fleet, but also one of the most advanced. Built for manoeuvrability, it is able to reach the highest warp speeds of any vessel of its time, and is designed for long-term exploration missions. Newly invented bio-neural gel packs are installed in ships of this class among other technological advances. These gel packs operate faster than traditional isolinear chips, making the ships' computers as quick as the vessels themselves.

Registry number

Hull constructed from tritanium alloy

CLASS-2 SHUTTLE

Cockpit is claustrophobic compared to other shuttle designs

Warp nacelle

Escape pod hatch

SHUTTLECRAFT

Voyager's complement of Class-2 shuttles bear a new streamlined design in Starfleet auxiliary spacecraft. Though they are highly advanced, these personnel transport shuttles were never intended for the rigours of supporting a lone starship in a dangerous sector of space. Their limitations force the design and construction of a new support vessel, the *Delta Flyer*, which begins as a personal project for the crew, uniting them in a common goal.

PLANETARY LANDINGS

Intrepid-class starships are one of the few ship designs in the fleet capable of entering a planet's atmosphere for a terrestrial landing. A risky proposition at the best of times, this manoeuvre is so rare that it is not unusual for Starfleet pilots to be completely unfamiliar with the process.

THE BRIDGE

Following the 24th century design trend of keeping the captain on even level with her crew, the command chair is seated beside the first officer's station at the centre of *Voyager*'s bridge. An expanded, single conn unit allows the pilot to control the helm operations and navigation while the traditional support stations ring the bridge bulkhead. The grey and metallic colouring of the interior is standard across Starfleet's new ship designs.

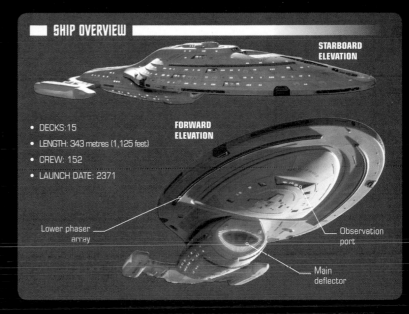

SHIP OVERVIEW

STARBOARD ELEVATION

FORWARD ELEVATION

- DECKS: 15
- LENGTH: 343 metres (1,125 feet)
- CREW: 152
- LAUNCH DATE: 2371

Lower phaser array

Observation port

Main deflector

NEELIX'S KITCHEN

With limitations set on *Voyager*'s food replicators to conserve energy, one of the ship's newest crewmembers, Neelix, converts the captain's private dining room into a kitchen. There, he works to create interesting delicacies from foods traded from aliens or grown in the airponics bay.

MESS HALL

Located off the captain's private dining room (and subsequent kitchen), the *Voyager* mess hall is both a dining room and a social gathering place on the ship for a crew that rarely gets shore leave. Events ranging from birthdays to classroom science fairs have been hosted here.

Bridge

Briefing Room

Mess hall

Captain Janeway's quarters

Upper phaser array

Upper sensor array

USS VOYAGER
NCC-74656

Reaction Control System (RCS) thrusters

Defensive shield grid

Secondary navigation deflector

Navigation beacon

CAPTAIN JANEWAY

THE CHILD OF A STARFLEET ADMIRAL, Kathryn Janeway rose through the ranks as a science officer before taking command of the *U.S.S. Voyager*. When the ill-fated ship becomes stranded in the Delta Quadrant, she finds herself in command of a combined crew of Starfleet personnel and rebel Maquis fighters. Janeway's tireless effort to integrate the crews and bring them safely home are rewarded when *Voyager* flies into San Francisco seven years after its abduction, and Janeway is promoted to admiral like her father.

Captain rank pips

Combadge (updated design)

A CAPTAIN ALONE

Isolated thousands of light years from the Federation, Captain Janeway remains resolute that *Voyager* will continue to function as a Starfleet ship, following the rules and regulations established by command. As much as Janeway is close to her crew, her position keeps her slightly apart from her subordinates. She left behind a fiancé when the ship was taken, only to learn that he has moved on when the crew are able to make temporary contact with the Alpha Quadrant. Janeway's time on the journey is spent navigating both the hazards of space and the complex relationships that form between her and her first officer, as well as aliens and even holograms, as she works to define a life far from her closest peer.

A CLASSIC MENTOR
Unable to contact her mentors within Starfleet, Janeway turns to the holodeck for guidance. A holographic recreation of the famed Renaissance artist and scientist Leonardo da Vinci provides counsel to Janeway as he challenges her to grow and expand her horizons with his classical training.

Collected sheet music for Mendelssohn's "Songs Without Words"

Horn

Elbow

Tone arm

Crank

Turntable

CLASSICAL MANUSCRIPT

Even in the Delta Quadrant, Starfleet uniform regulations are strictly followed

A TOUCH OF HOME
Janeway may never have learned to play an instrument, but music has always been important to the captain. Janeway's personal quarters are decorated with touches of Earth's past, keeping her linked both to home and her interests, including music, ballet and black coffee.

VINTAGE GRAMOPHONE

TECHNICAL DIFFICULTIES

As part of her decision to continue commanding her ship under Starfleet rules and regulations, Janeway insists on adhering to the Prime Directive ordering non-interference in alien cultures. This proves difficult, as *Voyager* was catapulted to an area of space inhabited by alien races who covet Starfleet's advanced technology. Knowing that any sharing of technology could tip the balance of power in the sector, the *Voyager* crew make many enemies as they struggle to cling to the Prime Directive. Janeway herself faces many challenges when following that rule conflicts with protecting her crew.

Touch-sensitive screen

Interfaces with tricorder for image projection and data transfer

Advanced *Intrepid*-class technology

CAPTAIN'S DESKTOP MONITOR

CAPTAIN'S READY ROOM
Captain Janeway's ready room is located just off the bridge. She has a formal meeting area for crew discussions, along with more casual seating off to the side of the room where she can sit back, relax and watch the stars pass by.

Desktop monitor

UNDER ATTACK
As the lone Starfleet ship in the Delta Quadrant, *Voyager* is under constant assault from enemy races. The crew are forced to defend their home by any means necessary without the benefit of reinforcements.

Capable of widespread burst for multiple targets

Power indicator

Prefire chamber

Dual emitters

Double-handed grip for increased stability

RATIONING TECHNOLOGY
With replicator use being rationed and limited resources available, the *Voyager* crew have to rely largely on the technology on hand, especially with regards to defensive weapons. This is another reason it is beneficial for them to refrain from sharing their equipment with alien species.

COMPRESSION PHASER RIFLE

JANEWAY AND THE BORG

With the possible exception of Jean-Luc Picard, no Starfleet captain has had as much experience with the Borg as Captain Janeway, since travelling through their space is necessary for *Voyager*'s journey home. A brief alliance with the Borg against a common enemy gives the crew a useful jump closer to the Alpha Quadrant, along with a new crewmember in a former Borg drone, Seven of Nine. Janeway's work in helping Seven of Nine's transition from her assimilation to reclaim her lost humanity becomes one of the captain's most challenging and rewarding relationships.

THE VOYAGE HOME

Almost every Starfleet captain is a hands-on leader, seeing no task as too small. For Janeway it has always been a matter of personal pride to do whatever needs to be done to complete a mission. This has served her well on the long trek home. The former science officer calls on all her knowledge and skills to command her crew through the unexplored Delta Quadrant, encountering new life and new civilizations and boldly going where no one has gone before.

CAPT. JANEWAY'S CREW

VOYAGER'S JOURNEY to the Delta Quadrant begins as a rescue mission. Captain Janeway in searching for a missing crewmate and friend, *Voyager*'s security officer, Tuvok, who is working undercover on a Maquis ship to expose a group of rebels. When the Maquis and Starfleet crews both become stranded in the Delta Quadrant, they are forced to put aside their differences and unite under the common cause of getting home.

B'ELANNA TORRES

Torres dropped out of Starfleet Academy in her second year under the belief that the intense emotions of her mixed Klingon/Human heritage would never mesh with Starfleet rules. Something of a lost soul, she found a mission with the Maquis as engineer on Chakotay's ship. When the two crews combine, she is a logical choice for the open position of *Voyager*'s chief engineer even though it means assigning her above other Starfleet officers. As she grows into her role, Torres works through her personal demons with the help of her new friends and future husband, Tom Paris.

Provisional officer lieutenant junior grade rank pin

SEVEN OF NINE

Annika Hansen spent her formative years as a Borg drone with the designation Seven of Nine, Tertiary Adjunct of Unimatrix 01, after she and her Human parents were assimilated by the Borg Collective. Seven, as she is later called, is chosen as the Borg liaison with the *Voyager* crew during a brief alliance, which ends abruptly with Captain Janeway severing the drone's connection to the Collective. In spite of many struggles, Seven relies on the crew to help her regain her humanity and fully disconnect from the Borg.

Tattoo in honour of Native American heritage

The doctor is able to remove most of Seven's Borg implants and restore her Human appearance

Ocular implant

Contains all standard tools

ENGINEERING FIELD KIT

CHAKOTAY

A man of strong Native American heritage and beliefs, Chakotay is one of a few Starfleet officers that abandoned the organization after what they felt was an unfair peace agreement between the Federation and the Cardassians. He then took up arms against his former leaders as a commander in the Maquis. It was his ship that Tuvok had infiltrated when they were abducted to the Delta Quadrant. When his ship is destroyed, Chakotay is forced into accepting Janeway's offer to merge the two crews and come together under her leadership on *Voyager*.

Blackbird's wing

CHAKOTAY'S MEDICINE BUNDLE

Engraved river rock

THE DOCTOR

The Emergency Medical Hologram (EMH) onboard *Voyager* is forced to expand its programming when the ship's entire medical staff are killed, leaving him in charge of sickbay. Known simply as "the doctor", he takes that initiative to heart, striving to become a fully formed individual. This growth is not always easy, as evidenced by his struggle to simply choose a name for himself. But he is able to broaden his horizons when a piece of futuristic technology – a mobile holo-emitter – allows him to escape the confines of sickbay and move out into the universe beyond.

Autonomous self-sustaining mobile holo-emitter

Sensor surface

Holographic depiction of Starfleet medical uniform

TR-590 TRICORDER X

An updated version of the Starfleet tricorder, the TR-590 is smaller and has several new design features including the ability to function in more hazardous environments than previous models.

Emergency upload

Data read-out

DIAGNOSTIC DEVICE

MEDICAL HAND SCANNER

Far from Starfleet medical supplies, the doctor must make do with the limited quantities of standard equipment that he has available.

Tuvok is 107 years old at the start of *Voyager*'s journey

TUVOK

The Vulcan chief of security is a friend and trusted advisor to Captain Janeway. The many experiences from his long life enable him to provide a different, more logical, perspective on their situation. After the *Voyager* and Maquis crews merge, Tuvok is initially at odds with the more emotional Maquis crewmembers who feel betrayed by his actions infiltrating their ship, but his calm Vulcan presence eventually helps him bond with the crew.

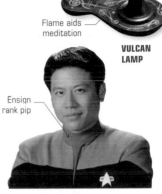

Flame aids meditation

VULCAN LAMP

Ensign rank pip

TOM PARIS

Tom Paris is imprisoned in a Federation penal settlement when Captain Janeway approaches him for help piloting her ship through the Badlands. The former Starfleet officer accepts her offer unaware that he is setting himself up for a tougher sentence trapped in the Delta Quadrant. Paris's relaxed attitude is an asset to the crew, as he sets up holodeck programs for rest and recreation.

HARRY KIM

The entire *Voyager* crew want to get home, but few embody that desire so visibly as Harry Kim, a San Francisco native who dearly misses his family. This is the operations officer's first posting, and he is proud to serve by taking all that he had learned at Starfleet Academy and putting it into practice. A model officer, he is also an enthusiastic sidekick in Tom Paris's plans.

Talaxians have two spinal columns

Ocampa female

KES AND NEELIX

Kes and Neelix are a unique couple from two different alien races native to the Delta Quadrant, who join *Voyager*'s crew shortly after the ship is pulled across the Galaxy. Kes contributes to the ship by assisting the doctor and creating an airponics bay to grow necessary food supplies, while Neelix wears many hats serving as chef, morale officer and a general guide to the Delta Quadrant and its inhabitants.

THE BORG COLLECTIVE

THE BORG ARE A RACE OF CYBERNETIC humanoids with a single focus: achieving a perfect society. They do this by assimilating other races into their Collective, adding cybernetic parts to enhance their bodies and joining their minds in a shared consciousness with billions of experiences. This Collective of minds and bodies work as one in the Borgs' mission to advance to the top of the evolutionary chain. The Borg have conquered thousands of worlds in their pursuit of perfection with the conviction that resistance is futile.

Organic material

Metal skull and spinal cord

Upper torso detachable from body

LOCUTUS OF BORG
As the Borg move into the Alpha Quadrant in the 24th century, they manage to capture and assimilate Captain Jean-Luc Picard of the *U.S.S. Enterprise*-D. In a rare show of individualism, they christen him "Locutus" and make him their spokesperson to the Federation. Using Picard's knowledge of Starfleet tactics, the Borg decimate Federation forces before the captain can be rescued.

IN SEARCH OF PERFECTION
The Borg seek out the biological and technological distinctiveness of other cultures for assimilation into their own, adapting their bodies and technology in their ultimate goal of achieving a perfect society.

Clamps hold two parts of body together

THE BORG QUEEN

The Borg Queen is the closest thing to an individual among the Collective, being both the voice that brings order to the chaos of billions of voices while also existing as the culmination of those minds. In much the way a community of bees on Earth functions with a multitude of drones in service to a queen, the Borg hive works in conjunction with their queen. It is rare for her to make herself known to outsiders. Even Captain Picard does not recall her influence during his time as Locutus, although he heard her voice among the many. Unlike her emotionless drones, the Borg Queen herself does show emotion. She uses seduction as her weapon, promising to fulfill her victims' desires as she takes over their minds.

Body is cybernetic

Regeneration alcove provides power for a drone's cybernetic implants

THE HIVE
Within each Borg ship the drones work in unison, communicating through a neural link implanted in their bodies. This allows them to share one mind with their "crewmates" as well as their entire race.

BORG CUBE

The Borg use distinctive cube-shaped ships with no centralized systems, such as a bridge or engineering section. Instead, the Borg Collective commands the ship from multiple points of access throughout the vessel. Adaptive shielding learns from each enemy attack to deflect subsequent firing, while regenerative hull plating automatically begins reconstruction in the midst of battle. In most cases, a single cube is sufficient to overpower an entire planet.

"Crew" of up to 130,000 drones

Neuro-processing adjunct

Neuro-transceiver (in upper spine)

Internal volume of 28 cubic kilometres (6.7 cubic miles)

Ocular implant reads entire EM spectrum

Travels via transwarp conduits

THE BATTLE OF WOLF 359
Starfleet sends a fleet of 40 ships to the Wolf 359 system to intercept the first Borg incursion to the Alpha Quadrant. Only one ship survives.

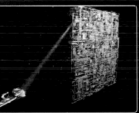

THE BORG IN COMBAT
The Borg are the toughest enemy the Federation has ever faced because they are a collection of its most powerful enemies and allies. When the Borg assimilate a person they have access to all knowledge contained in the individual. This makes them formidable fighters able to exploit known weaknesses and defend against expected attacks.

Exo-plating protects drone from physical attacks

Ablative hull armour

Capable of generating a rift in the space-time continuum

BORG DRONES

Borg drones, like their ships, are fully adaptive defensive machines that quickly learn from a single experience and share their knowledge throughout the Collective. The first time a weapon is used against a drone the strike is recorded and adapted to so that other Borg will be able to shield against similar attacks. Borg drones come from thousands of races, assimilated into one mind. Each drone is equipped with assimilation nanoprobes they can inject into aliens bodies to begin the conversion process. Once the nanoprobes take over, the body rapidly changes, with new cybernetic technology erupting from the skin and taking control as the victim's mind joins with the Collective.

Adaptable force field makes drone resistant to energy weapons

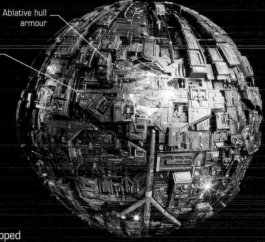

BORG SPHERE
The sphere ship design is first seen during an attack on Earth by a Borg cube in the year 2373. At the point Starfleet thinks they have gained the upper hand, a sphere ejects from the larger vessel and escapes through time with the *Enterprise*-E in pursuit.

BORG REBELS AND RENEGADES

THE BORG SHARE A SINGLE CONSCIOUSNESS with billions of voices working together toward a common goal. The overwhelming majority of these beings were assimilated unwillingly, trapped forever into this single-mindedness. In rare cases – often with Federation intervention – some drones have been able to break free of the Collective and regain their personalities, at least for a limited time. These few renegade Borg and the communities they have formed in an effort to weaken the Collective serve as proof that resistance is not always futile.

HUGH
After discovering a crashed Borg ship, the crew of the *Enterprise*-D are temporarily able to separate a drone from the Collective. After interacting with the Starfleet crew, the drone learns the concept of individuality and adopts the name "Hugh".

UNIMATRIX ZERO

A genetic mutation affecting one in a million Borg allowed for the creation of a virtual world free from the Collective, where drones can exist for a brief time as individuals. While their bodies regenerate, the minds of these fortunate drones transfer to this virtual construct, called Unimatrix Zero, where they can assume the appearances they possessed prior to being assimilated. The *Voyager* crew makes contact with Unimatrix Zero through the ex-drone Seven of Nine, and formulates a plan to exploit the mutation to break the drones free permanently. But they are forced to destroy Unimatrix Zero when the Borg Queen discovers the plan and begins killing all of the drones involved.

A BORG UTOPIA
Precisely how the virtual reality of Unimatrix Zero came into existence is not clear. Drones who can enter it are only aware of its existence while they are regenerating, and will lose all knowledge of it when their regeneration cycle is complete.

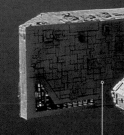

Ship's systems encased in armour, unlike standard cube

SEVEN OF NINE
Seven of Nine's careful reintegration into society is one of the most successful acts of rebellion against the Borg Collective in the 24th century.

The Borg queen sends "virtual" drones into Unimatrix Zero to find a way to destroy it

LORE

When Hugh is released from the *Enterprise*-D and reintegrated into the Collective he carries his newfound independence with him, infecting the Borg in his cube with a taste of individuality. The group become separated from the Collective and are lost without purpose until a chance encounter with Dr Noonien Soong's failed creation, the android Lore. Taking command of these rogue Borg, Lore gives them individual names, and promises them a new search for perfection as artificial life-forms like himself. The drones then carve a path of destruction through Federation space.

HUGH'S REBELLION

Hugh, now part of Lore's crew, sows the seeds of further rebellion when he realizes that Lore has his own agenda in working with the renegade Borg – he is setting a trap for his "brother", Data. With the help of the *Enterprise*-D crew, Hugh and a small band of rebels thwart Lore's plan and free themselves from his rule.

Hypothesised that Type 03 may be an alien vessel assimilated by the Borg

Heavily armed

THE RENEGADE SHIP

This Borg ship of unknown origin is only encountered by the Federation once, during the interaction between the *Enterprise*-D and the renegade group of Borg under the leadership of the android Lore. Designated as a Borg Type 03 vessel, because it is the third type of Borg ship encountered by Starfleet, it is notable for its asymmetrical design that does not match the basic cube or sphere shapes of other Borg ships.

Multiple times larger than a *Galaxy*-class starship

Forward weapons

BORG SHIP TYPE 03

SEPARATION FROM THE COLLECTIVE

In 2376, as the Starship *Voyager* crosses through Borg space, its crew encounter a small group of assimilated youth that they are able to free from the Collective. The Starfleet crew adopt these children, and Seven of Nine takes an active role in helping them to readjust into society. Most of the children are either returned home or are adopted by an alien family, but the last remaining adolescent, Icheb, returns to the Alpha Quadrant with *Voyager* and is accepted into Starfleet Academy.

Some of Seven of Nine's Borg implants can never be removed

Travels via transwarp conduits

ADOLESCENT BORG

Borg maturation chambers accelerate growth rates to 25 times that of typical humanoid development. The Borg emerge from these chambers after 17 cycles to begin service to the Collective, in groups that are generally led by the first of the drones to exit its chamber.

BORG MATURATION CHAMBERS

Infants and young children assimilated by the Borg have no place in their society as they are not considered capable of providing for the needs of the Collective. As such, these lesser drones are raised in maturation chambers until they have reached maturity and can contribute to the Collective.

THE OCAMPA

A COMPASSIONATE Delta Quadrant race, the Ocampa are on their own for the first time in a millennium. Long ago, an advanced alien species known as the Nacene accidentally caused an ecological disaster on the Ocampa homeworld. Full of remorse, they created a safe living environment beneath the surface for the Ocampa to live in. When the sole remaining Nacene caretaker begins to die after 1,000 years of stewardship over the Ocampa, he pulls aliens from across the Galaxy – including the crew of the *U.S.S. Voyager* – to find a suitable replacement to watch over them.

Latent psychic abilities

Ocampa at age of three

THE OCAMPA HOMEWORLD
With the same name as the species that dwells on it, the planet Ocampa was once a fertile Class-M world. When the Nacene visited it, their ships accidentally stripped the planet's atmosphere of nucleogenic particles, making rainfall impossible and turning the surface into a lifeless desert. The Ocampa know this event as "the warming".

THE ELOGIUM
A female Ocampan's time of sexual maturation is known as the *elogium*. During this phase – usually between the fourth and fifth years of life – the body undergoes a series of major physiological changes, with side effects including fever, perspiration, anxiety, paranoia, changes of eye color and an increased heart rate.

AIRPONICS
Kes is able to adapt lessons she had learned from living underground on a desert planet to create a combination airponics and hydroponics bay on *Voyager*, for growing plants in a moist air environment rather than in typical soil. Her vegetables become an important staple of the crew's diet.

KES
Kes is the first of her people in generations to leave their homeworld and explore the stars, when her curiosity drives her to join the crew of the *U.S.S. Voyager*. Since Ocampa typically have a lifespan of only nine years, the time she spends on *Voyager* significantly changes her both emotionally and physically. Chief among her encounters is a reunion with a sect of Ocampa who left their world centuries earlier with another Nacene entity that had been keeping watch over them. Out in the universe, these Ocampa were able to evolve beyond their limitations, tapping into their latent psychokinetic powers and even doubling their lifespan – two things that were previously thought to be impossible.

THE TALAXIANS

TALAXIANS ARE A GENIAL SPECIES, with much of the populace possessing a well-developed sense of whimsy and lightheartedness. This is in spite of a dark history as survivors of a vicious war with the Haakonian Order, which sent their people fleeing from their homeworld of Talax in search of a safe haven. This ancient race has been exploring the Delta Quadrant for centuries longer than Humans have been traveling through their own sector of space, but they still retain a spirituality that has hardly been influenced by their scientific advancement.

IN THE KITCHEN WITH NEELIX
Talaxians believe in sharing the history of a meal before eating as a way of enhancing the dining experience. After joining the *Voyager* crew, Neelix takes this tradition to heart in his role as chef, one of several positions he creates to make himself useful to the crew while helping to extend the ship's limited resources.

A NEW HOME
When *Voyager* encounters a small colony of Talaxian ex-patriots thousands of light years from their homeworld, the crew does what they can to assist the race in defending themselves against an alien menace. It soon becomes clear that the colonists need a leader to protect them once the *Voyager* has gone, prompting Neelix to stay behind.

**TALAXIAN FEMALE
*ALIXIA***

Spots cover bodies of both males and females

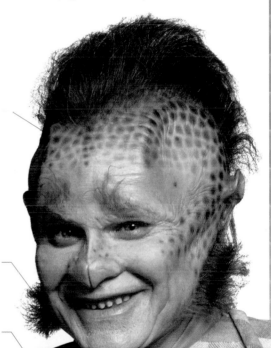

Whiskers on males are very sensitive

Dense musculature on the upper body

FAMILY BONDS
Talaxians are a tightly bonded people, and the loss of his family haunted Neelix for many years. The new family Neelix finds in the Talaxian colony never replaces the relations who were killed by the Haakonians, such as his sister Alixia, or the friends he made on *Voyager*, but they give him a purpose he has not felt in years. Neelix finds contentment with his people after he leaves *Voyager* and gains a role as *Voyager*'s permanent ambassador to the Delta Quadrant.

NEELIX

Neelix was the lone member of his family to survive a devastating attack by the Haakonian Order, simply by being in the right place at the right time. He has since made it his mission to survive by any means necessary, proving himself useful to those around him, or doing what needs to be done even when it means operating on the wrong side of the law. He does it all with a typical Talaxian enthusiasm to smile through tragedy and make the best of a bad situation, even one of his own making.

THE KAZON

KAZON DISRUPTOR RIFLE

Prefire chamber

Weapons have an unsophisticated design

Weathered by the elements

THE KAZON WERE FIRST set against one another by a species called the Trabe who enslaved them, and encouraged infighting between the Kazon sects as a way of maintaining control. The Kazon suffered under the oppressive rule of the Trabe for years until they were able to unite and overthrow their oppressors. Once they had obtained their freedom, however, tensions between the sects re-emerged as they fought for control. The number of sects is ever-changing, and power is constantly shifting among these Delta Quadrant factions.

Trigger button

KAZON WEAPONS
Despite its crude appearance, Kazon weaponry can be devastatingly effective. Lacking a stun setting, a hit from a Kazon weapon will usually severely wound or kill a target.

Lacks any form of sighting aid

Often constructed from scavanged items

KAZON PISTOL

KAZON SHIPS
Most Kazon vessels originally belonged to the Trabe and were taken in their defeat. Though they are technologically advanced, in combat they are generally inferior to Federation vessels, and individually, Kazon ships pose little threat against an *Intrepid*-class starship.

Bridge

Reinforced hull armour

Plasma torpedo launcher

Sections of hair grow in clumps

Warp nacelle

PREDATOR-CLASS WARSHIP

1,800 metres long

MARK OF THE ORDER
The Mark of the Kazon Order is the unifying symbol for a race that has few united experiences. As of the year 2372 approximately 18 sects exist that identify themselves by joining the Kazon moniker with their tribal name. Some of the more powerful factions are the Kazon-Ogla, Kazon-Nistrim and Kazon-Relora.

KAZON SOCIETY
The Kazon are a violent and patriarchal society. A leader within a sect is known as a *Maje* with the highest rank in a sect being First *Maje*. Like other species that have suffered under oppression, the Kazon have evolved into a fiercely territorial warrior race. When young Kazon men come of age they are subjected to a trial in which they earn their adult name through the killing of an enemy or their own honoured death in battle. The adult name is generally an extension of their birth name with the addition of the title *Jal*.

Clothing of the Ogla sect

KAZON SECTS
Each of the Kazon sects adorn their soldiers in uniforms unique to their individual tribe as one of the many ways they differentiate themselves from one another. Since natural resources are scarce in their sector, each sect has control over different materials, which is often the cause of border conflicts and infighting.

THE VIDIIANS

THIS PROUD DELTA QUADRANT RACE, once known for its arts and culture, has been completely redefined by the horrific disease from which it has suffered for the last 2,000 years. Since the dreaded Phage affliction struck its people, the central government, the Vidiian Sodality, has devoted all its resources to fighting the disease and sustaining the lives of its dying population through constant organ transplantation. At first, organs were taken from the dead, but as the disease worsened the Vidiians moved on to stealing organs from living victims.

THE PHAGE
The Phage virus destroys the body by affecting the genetic codes of its victims and attacking them on a cellular level. For centuries, the only known method of fighting the illness has been to replace the infected organs. This is not a cure, but it manages to hold off death for as long as possible.

VIDIIAN SHIPS
Vidiian ships are designed to minimize the need for personal interaction, protecting the crew against the spread of the Phage virus. The average bridge only requires a pair of crewmembers, typically a commander and a *honatta* – an organ harvesting specialist – to maintain control of the vessel. The ships are very powerfully armed, carrying hypothermic charges to disable targeted vessels, allowing them to be boarded and the crews' organs harvested.

Bridge

Impulse engines

Particle beam weapon

Grapplers deploy from underside

Warp nacelle

VIDIIAN WARSHIP

MEDICAL EQUIPMENT

The Vidiian bio-probe is one of the most advanced pieces of hand-held technology ever encountered by a Federation crew. This single device can conduct a biological scan down to the microcellular level, stun a victim and harvest their organs by transporting them directly out of the body. It is the main instrument of a *honatta*.

Organ harvesting surgical instrument

Neural resonator stuns victims

Quantum imaging scanner

Bioneural circuitry supplements higher brain functions

Diseased skin

BY ANY MEANS NECESSARY
Their pressing need for replacement organs has turned the Vidiians into a race to be feared, and taking organs and skin from many different alien species has given them a truly horrifying appearance. Many Vidiians are opposed to the violence but they are powerless to stop it.

DR DANARA PEL
Not all Vidiians endorse the aggressive behaviour of their race. Dr Danara Pel is one medical expert more focused on finding a cure than expending effort on saving individuals. *Voyager*'s doctor saves her life by treating her with Klingon DNA, which proves resistant to the Phage. Sadly, Dr Pel is forced to leave the doctor, for whom she has developed feelings, to continue her work. Years after the pair's parting, the *Voyager* crew learn that the Phage has reportedly been cured by an alien think tank, allowing the Vidiians to return to normal lives.

THE HIROGEN

THE HIROGEN ARE A NOMADIC RACE that travels the Delta Quadrant as hunters in search of prey. Each pack is led by an Alpha-Hirogen who takes command of the hunt and is deferred to on all decisions. These packs can consist of as few as two members – an Alpha and a Beta-Hirogen – on a single vessel or incorporate several ships. The hunt has been their way of life for a thousand years, causing them to abandon their homeworld in search of more challenging prey.

Helmet

BETA-HIROGEN

Heightened immune system

Acute sensory perception

A RACE OF HUNTERS

Hirogen society is consumed by the hunt. It is how they define themselves. All scientific and technological advancement has ceased among their people except where it pertains to the hunt. They have no known alliances or affiliations beyond their packs as all other alien races are simply seen as prey. The Hirogen have great traditions and rituals associated with the hunt, both in preparation for the fight and after the kill.

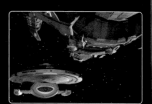

HIROGEN AND VOYAGER
A series of ancient Hirogen relay stations allows the *Voyager* crew to communicate with Starfleet, but the price of becoming targets for the hunters is almost too high.

Life support system

HIROGEN WEAPONS
The Hirogen have turned their entire technological advancement toward creating weapons for the hunt. Their ships are heavily armed and their energy weapons are powerful, but they also retain a large selection of knives and blades for close combat.

Body armour

Hirogen are much larger than an average humanoid

Alien skull

Mounted on vessels' interior in ritualistic fashion

Tool prepares prey for the kill

PREY
Unusual relics are prized among the Hirogen, with skeletons and body parts proudly displayed on their ships.

HUNTING TROPHIES

PAINT

Application of paint to the face and helmet is an important ritual of hunt preparation. It is equally significant for the prey as a hunter will often adorn his captives as well. If paint is unavailable, the hunter will still go through the motions of the ritual.

HUNTING PAINT

SPECIES 8472

SPECIES 8472 IS THE BORG DESIGNATION for a race that resides in fluidic space, a dimension separate from the known universe. The true name of this species is unknown even after several encounters with the *Voyager* crew. Species 8472 is initially seen as an enemy of the Federation largely due to misunderstandings caused by a brief alliance between the *Voyager* crew and the Borg. Ultimately Captain Janeway is able to negotiate peace and avert a potential invasion of the Alpha Quadrant.

Constructed from organic technology

Primary energy weapon

SPECIES 8472 BIOSHIP

WAR WITH THE BORG
When the Borg invaded fluidic space they discovered that this powerful alien species was resistant to their assimilation techniques. Species 8472 followed them back to the Delta Quadrant and began wiping out Borg installations.

Communicates telepathically

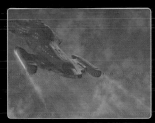

FLUIDIC SPACE
Species 8472 inhabits a completely separate dimension composed of organic fluid matter, which is very different from the traditional vacuum of space.

Claws are primary weapons

8472 PHYSIOLOGY

Species 8472 is a non-humanoid race with highly advanced biogenetically engineered technology, which made them a tempting target for the Borg. Their dense genetic structure and incredibly strong immune system, however, allows their bodies to reject all attempts at assimilation. Their cells can even be used as a weapon, infecting a victim and consuming their body from the inside out. When Species 8472 retaliates against the Borg, a brief alliance between the Borg and the *Voyager* crew results in the creation of nanoprobe weapons that provide the only known defence against the race.

Can survive in vacuum of space

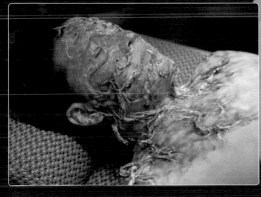

"THE WEAK WILL PERISH"
Species 8472 use their claws to attack victims, infecting them with their cells that contain densely packed DNA in a triple helix formation. These alien cells then destroy the victim's own cells. The only known cure is the use of Borg nanoprobes injected into the victim's bloodstream.

Tripedal

LONDON, NEW YORK, MELBOURNE, MUNICH and DELHI

For Dorling Kindersley

Editor David Fentiman
Designers Toby Truphet, Mark Richards, Lisa Robb
Senior Designer Robert Perry
Managing Editor Laura Gilbert
Design Manager Maxine Pedliham
Art Director Ron Stobbart
Publishing Director Simon Beecroft
Pre-Production Producer Rebecca Fallowfield
Senior Producer Shabana Shakir

For CBS

Vice President of Product Development
John Van Citters
Product Development Manager
Marian Cordry

This edition published in 2014
First published in Great Britain in 2013 by
Dorling Kindersley Limited
80 Strand, London WC2R ORL

008-185659-Mar/13

A CIP catalogue record for this book
is available from the British Library.

ISBN: 978-0-2411-8030-3

Colour reproduction by Altaimage, UK
Printed and bound in China by Hung Hing

Picture credit:
6-7 NASA: JPL-Caltech

Author's Acknowledgments:

Thanks to everyone at CBS Consumer Products and Dorling Kindersley,
especially Marian Cordry, David Fentiman, Laura Gilbert, Risa Kessler,
Toby Truphet, and John Van Citters.

The publisher would like to thank:

Anna Reinbold and Sunita Gahir,
NASA for space imagery

Discover more at
www.dk.com